A BOOK OF VERSE

FOR BOYS AND GIRLS

COMPILED BY

J. C. SMITH

A NEW EDITION
WITH MANY MODERN POEMS
PART III

OXFORD
AT THE CLARENDON PRESS

Oxford University Press, Ely House, London W. 1

GLASGOW NEW YORK TORONTO MELBOURNE WELLINGTON
CAPE TOWN SALISBURY IBADAN NAIROBI LUSAKA ADDIS ABABA
BOMBAY CALCUTTA MADRAS KARACHI LAHORE DACCA
KUALA LUMPUR HONG KONG TOKYO

NEW EDITION (TWENTY-SEVENTH IMPRESSION) 1927
REPRINTED 1929, 1932, 1936, 1947, 1948, 1951, 1956, 1961
1966
PRINTED IN GREAT BRITAIN

PREFACE TO PART III

STEVENSON says somewhere that any man who could really remember his boyhood might write an incomparable book. Certainly he would have a main advantage for making an Anthology; and in making this one I must not deny that I have founded on the poems that delighted me when I was a boy.

But opportunities were limited, and memory fails, and good verse has been written since then. So I have tried to supplement my own recollections by observing the tastes of a younger generation.

Even this is not enough. We cannot go altogether by taste; for children sometimes like what is not good for them. We must ask, after all, 'What poems ought children to read?' 'What can poetry do for them?'

Can it strengthen the memory, for example, as we used to be told? The theory collapses at the question 'What memory?' to which there seems to be no ready answer, except perhaps 'The memory for poetry'. For you may learn all Shakespeare by heart, and it will not help you very obviously to remember a tune, or a date, or a short cut, or the rule for extracting the cube root. The memory theory comes then to this, that we learn poetry in order to learn more poetry—a doubtful but an innocent conclusion.

Not so innocent in effect is the view implied in those collections which aim at 'illustrating' (as they call it) 'the course of literature'. Plausible to examinees, this view is yet essentially preposterous. It means that the purpose of poetry is to illustrate its own history. And this is, literally, preposterous; for unless poetry has some value of its own, its history can have none.

More respect is due to the heresy, held by all the Greeks before Aristotle, that poetry is a means of moral training. Yet, in its cruder or 'cautionary' form at least, this view is exposed to the objection that good poetry cannot, as a matter of fact, be written on that plan. And if this objection weighs lightly on the moralist, there is another which must appeal to him and is fatal to his view in any form—the objection, namely, that people are made good not by reading good poetry but by doing good deeds. On a purely ideal diet sentimentalism may thrive, but not morality. Tourguenieff's story of the Russian Countess, who weeps over a pitiful tale in her carriage while her coachman freezes to death on the box—that parable disposes of the moralistic heresy once for all. How can that be the end of an art which it accomplishes so imperfectly?

We must conclude that poetry is not a means to any-thing. It is one of the simple goods of life, and no more needs to be vindicated than the contemplation of a sunset or the intercourse of friends.

But we are not therefore shut up to the pedantry of 'Art for Art's sake'. Poetry is only one of the goods of life: it must not be pursued to the impoverishment of the whole. It may be that there is no real rivalry between the various elements of human perfection, that beauty and goodness are radically one. But practically, and for us, the moral and the aesthetic value of a poem can be distinguished as readily as the smell and the colour of a flower. Nor need we always tolerate the one for the sake of the other. The Stinking Gladdon is a handsome blossom; but we do not grow it in our drawing-rooms.

Between these rival claims—if they are rivals—the free adult may choose for himself. But we must choose for the children. The moralist must stand at the gate of our Paradise, and admit no poems ' but such as breathe content and virtue '.[1]

In poetry admitted on these terms he will find an ally, but no servant. Not by direct instruction, not by inculcating moral precepts, does poetry promote the cause of virtue, but by deepening and enriching the emotional soil in which the virtues flower. Like a health-giving breeze, in Plato's simile, the effluence of its beauty steals into ear and eye, and insensibly draws the soul into harmony with the beauty of reason.

All this, it will be said, amounts to an admission that, in childhood at least, poetry *is* after all a means. And so, in a sense, it is. For in childhood the capacity for rational enjoyment is still forming ; and poetry, which will help to fill that capacity, must also help to form it. But even in childhood, we must maintain, poetry is an effective means only in so far as it is already an end. It promotes the moralist's business by minding its own, which is to delight. For Poesy, in Dryden's golden words, ' only instructs as it delights '.

For all readers, and for young readers most of all, the delight which poetry gives lies largely in the music of the verse. Cowley indeed puts another element forward. ' I was infinitely delighted ', he tells us, ' with the stories of the knights and giants, and monsters, and brave horses which I found everywhere there (though my understanding had little to do with all this); and by degrees

---

[1] The phrase is E. Fitzgerald's.

with the tinkling of the rhyme and dance of the numbers.'
But Cowley was twelve when he thus made acquaintance
with the intricate harmonies of the *Faerie Queene* : to
younger children, and with simpler measures, the rhymes
and numbers very likely count for more. Very young
children indeed find pleasure in mere jingles, with no
apparent sense at all.

The first thing, then, that poetry can do for children is
to gratify and cultivate their feeling for verse. An ear
for verse, however, is not quite the same thing as an ear
for music. Many good poets, though perhaps none of
the very greatest, have had little or no sense of tune.

But the delight which poetry gives is never, or never
for long, merely sensuous. Verse itself is a special form
of emotional speech. Strong emotion tends to vent itself
in reiteration or recurrence. ' O Absalom ! my son,
my son Absalom ! '—' But mine, and mine I loved, and
mine I praised ! '—the grief that speaks in these reitera-
tions relieves the over-fraught heart like a rhythmic sob.
And it is on the rhythm, in fact, more generally than on
the words, that emotion produces this reiterative effect.
On this the poets have seized, and consecrated metre, or
recurrent rhythm, to the use of poetry. To our ears this
is the sole essential mark of verse. But the poets have
found out many embellishments—parallelism, rhyme,
alliteration, assonance, refrain—and some of these have
at different times been thought no less essential than
metre itself. This was perhaps due to the imperfect
state of the art, which needed these aids to reinforce the
rhythm. So I have known children refuse the name of
poetry to unrhymed verse, ' because it did not match,' they
said—did not give them, that is, the full pleasure that
they ask from poetry. All these charms are woven into

the spell of the best English verse, and to them it owes much of its power. Now these embellishments are all forms of recurrence, as the coloured parts which adorn a flower are all modifications of the leaf. And recurrence, we saw, is a sign of emotion—not of crude or immediate feeling, but of emotion controlled, tranquillized, beautified. To arouse such emotion is the second and chief aim of poetry.

The poet's fine ear and capacity of emotion belong to a nature unusually sensitive of impressions, and quick, under stress of feeling, to revive them in imagination. All lovers of poetry have these gifts in a measure; the poet has them in such measure that they must find utterance in coloured and rhythmic speech. By his very name the poet is a maker, a creator; he makes a new world to his heart's desire. True, he creates after Nature; with her hues and forms he invests his thoughts. Yet these forms are not mere garments of poetic thought; rather they are its living flesh. The poet does not put his thoughts into images; he thinks in images.

At first, as Cowley says, the understanding has little to do with all this. But presently the understanding too asserts its claim, and demands that these images shall be connected into an intelligible whole, that they shall, as we say, make sense. Thus poetry is distinguished from mere reverie or dream, and the greater forms of poetry from the lesser. Coleridge may have dreamed *Kubla Khan*: he did not dream *The Ancient Mariner*.

These four elements—sound, emotion, imagery, thought —are present in all good poetry. But they have no separate existence in our actual enjoyment of a poem, or in that original act of creation which our enjoyment faintly re-enacts. We analyse them out of the poem;

but no alchemy of ours could recombine them into that living whole. What fuses them into one is the poet's emotion, the poetic mood. This mood may be induced in various ways—by a sense-impression, by a recollection, by meditation on a theme. Sometimes it is actually induced by a rhythmic sound. This happens most often in those poems which are most nearly akin to mere reverie or dream. If Coleridge dreamed *Kubla Khan*, he dreamed it to the rhythm of a sonorous sentence from Purchas. And, if not actually induced by a rhythm, the poetic mood must always find its appropriate rhythm before it can beat itself out into imagery and thought. Wordsworth's *Solitary Reaper* supplies an unambiguous instance. That poem was suggested—we may almost say it was inspired—by this sentence from Wilkinson's *Tour of Scotland*:

' Passed a female who was reaping alone : she sung in Erse as she bended over her sickle ; the sweetest human voice I ever heard ; her strains were tenderly melancholy, and felt delicious, long after they were heard no more.'

This lovely picture caught the poet's eye : the rhythm of the last phrase filled his ear : from the memory of his own recent tour in Scotland an appropriate setting floated up. He saw himself mounting the side of a glen, on a still and cloudless day of Autumn, all things favouring the poetic mood. Suddenly from a field below there rises the voice of song. He looks down : the singer and her strain define themselves ; and his mood is precipitated into poetry. Swift to seek likeness in difference, imagination sweeps away to far other scenes where the same elements might meet—the music, the stillness, the cloudless blue—to Arabian oases vocal with the nightingale, to Western Isles where the cuckoo's first note is heard in the blue hush of an April noon. I need not pursue the analysis. We see how the mood and the rhythm, happily wedded, prompt and guide the sequence of thought, the movement of imagination, and the choice of words.

These elements, I infer, should prompt and guide us in our choice and arrangement of poetry for the young. Thought and imagery are of the first importance, but as principles of selection their value is, on the whole, negative. Plainly we must not present children with thoughts and images which they cannot grasp or realize at all ; and this suggests a gradation in order of difficulty. But it does not follow that the children need comprehend the full meaning of every poem they are to enjoy, or apprehend every image with scientific precision. On the contrary, in the best poetry there seems always to be something— ' one thought, one grace, one wonder '—that hovers just beyond our grasp. And this suggests another reflection. Some poems have lost their power upon us because we have outgrown their ideas. But what is trite to us may seem fresh and profound to children. So we shall not scruple to include many pieces to which, for their commonplace ideas, a mature taste would refuse the name of classics.

On one thing, however, we shall insist as strictly as the makers of more classical anthologies, namely, on metrical excellence. But it will be a simple sort of excellence, not too elaborate in structure, though rich in those embellishments of which we have spoken, and one of which, at least, we saw that most children find indispensable.

But for positive guidance we must look chiefly to the element of emotion. Some emotions the moralist will veto ; others, very important to him, have no real interest for the poet, inasmuch as they have no value unless translated into action: of this nature is shame. Terror and pity in the full tragic sense are adult emotions; but death and suffering cannot be ignored even in childhood; nor need they be, provided that the fact of death is glorified by heroic circumstance or veiled by imaginative treatment. And, generally, in those emotions which reach pleasure through pain, we must beware that the pain does not overwhelm the pleasure.

Love, again, belongs to adult or adolescent life. Yet to omit all love poetry would seem to many like taking the spring out of the year. Such rigour is needless; for children can to some extent enter, as it were by anticipation, into states of feeling which they have not yet experienced. Here, then, the duty of poetry is to prepare the temple, by presenting the theme first in pure and chivalrous instances. No difficulty arises about poems in which love appears merely as a motive to actions properly interesting in themselves.

With all these cautions and exceptions there yet remains a wide range of expansive emotions to choose from. 'We live by admiration, hope, and love'; and by other feelings too, less august, but hardly less vital and delightful—by wonder and sympathy, by joy in the beauty of nature, by the spirit of comradeship and adventure, even by merriment and fun. The anthologist's business is to select such poems as will leave no considerable part of this emotional range untouched—and to arrange them so that a reader may pass from one poem to the next with no unpleasant break in the prevailing mood. For practical corollaries as to the way in which these poems should be studied I must refer to the Prefaces to Parts I and II.

The staff of the Clarendon Press has been at some

pains to furnish true texts. Of ballads there is no true
text; I have chosen what best suited my purpose, pre-
ferring (for instance) the Addisonian *Chevy Chase* as
smoother, easier, and no less vigorous than that older
ballad which so moved Sidney. In Blake's *Tiger* I have
returned to Malkin's reading—

> What dread hand forged thy dread feet?

The version in the *Songs of Experience* owes its survival,
I now believe, to no reason more profound than Blake's
dislike to destroy the plate.

J. C. SMITH.

[I have to thank Canon Beeching for permission to include
'Going down Hill on a Bicycle'; Mr. Laurence Binyon for
'Pine Trees'; Mr. Rudyard Kipling and Messrs. Methuen
& Co. for 'L'Envoi'; Sir H. Newbolt for 'Drake's Drum';
and Mr. W. B. Yeats for 'The Lake Isle of Innisfree': also
Messrs. D. Nutt & Co. for Henley's 'England, my England';
Messrs. Chatto & Windus for Stevenson's 'Requiem' and
'The Vagabond'; Mr. Bertram Dobell for James Thomson's
'Gifts' and 'In the Train'; and the proprietors of Browning's
copyrights for '*Lux in Tenebris*'.

Acknowledgements for leave to include copyright poems in
this new edition are due to Mr. Laurence Binyon and the proprietors of *The Times* for 'For the Fallen'; Mr. Basil Blackwell
for Mrs. Fredegond Shove's 'The New Ghost'; Mr. Robert
Bridges for 'Since Maurice died', 'London Snow', and
'There is a Hill'; Messrs. Duckworth & Co. for Mr. Hilaire
Belloc's 'The South Country'; Mr. Dudley Clark and the
proprietors of *The Times* for 'Called up'; Mr. W. W. Gibson
and Messrs. Elkin Mathews for 'Flannan Isle' and 'The

Stone ', and the latter also for Maurice Hewlett's ' Night-Errantry '; Mr. Robert Graves and Mr. Martin Secker for ' Rocky Acres ' from *Country Sentiment,* and the latter also for J. E. Flecker's ' The Old Ships ' from *Collected Poems*; Mr. Thomas Hardy for ' Friends Beyond ', ' Men who march away (1914) ', and ' When I set out for Lyonnesse '; the poet's family for Gerard Hopkins's ' Inversnaid '; Professor A. E. Housman and Mr. Grant Richards for ' Epitaph on an Army of Mercenaries ' from *Last Poems*; Mr. Rudyard Kipling and Messrs. Methuen & Co. for ' Sussex ' from *The Five Nations*; Messrs. Macmillan & Co. for Mr. Ralph Hodgson's ' The Song of Honour '; Mr. Walter de la Mare for ' An Epitaph ' and ' The Listeners '; Mr. John Masefield for ' Sea-Fever ' and ' Cargoes '; Miss Charlotte Mew and the Poetry Bookshop for ' *Exspecto Resurrectionem* '; Mr. Wilfrid Meynell for Mrs. Meynell's ' Christ in the Universe ', and Francis Thompson's ' In no Strange Land '; Miss Moira O'Neill and Messrs. Blackwood & Sons for ' Birds '; Mr. Robert Nichols and Messrs. Chatto & Windus for ' At the Wars '; Messrs. Sidgwick & Jackson for ' The Soldier ' from Rupert Brooke's *Collected Poems*; Professor Sorley for Charles Sorley's ' The Song of the Ungirt Runners '; Mrs. R. A. Taylor for ' The Quietist '; Mrs. Thomas for Edward Thomas's ' Adlestrop '; and Messrs. Macmillan & Co. for Tennyson's ' Crossing the Bar '.—J. C. SMITH.]

CONTENTS

I

IV

V

VI

VII

[241]

INDEX OF AUTHORS IN PART III

I

Matin Song

PACK, clouds, away! and welcome, day!
  With night we banish sorrow.
Sweet air, blow soft; mount, lark, aloft
  To give my Love good-morrow!
Wings from the wind to please her mind,
  Notes from the lark I'll borrow:
Bird, prune thy wing! nightingale, sing!
  To give my Love good-morrow!
      To give my Love good-morrow
      Notes from them all I'll borrow.

Wake from thy nest, robin red-breast!
  Sing, birds, in every furrow!
And from each bill let music shrill
  Give my fair Love good-morrow!
Blackbird and thrush, in every bush,
  Stare, linnet, and cock-sparrow,
You pretty elves, among yourselves
  Sing my fair Love good-morrow!
      To give my Love good-morrow
      Sing, birds, in every furrow!

THOMAS HEYWOOD (1580?–1650?)

Stare] Starling.

Aubade

HARK! hark! the lark at heaven's gate sings,
    And Phoebus 'gins arise,
His steeds to water at those springs
    On chaliced flowers that lies;
And winking Mary-buds begin
    To ope their golden eyes:
With everything that pretty is,
    My lady sweet, arise!
       Arise, arise!

           WILLIAM SHAKESPEARE (1564–1616)

Aubade

THE lark now leaves his wat'ry nest,
    And climbing shakes his dewy wings.
He takes this window for the East,
    And to implore your light he sings—
Awake, awake! the morn will never rise
Till she can dress her beauty at your eyes.

The merchant bows unto the seaman's star,
    The ploughman from the sun his season takes;
But still the lover wonders what they are
    Who look for day before his mistress wakes.
Awake, awake! break thro' your veils of lawn!
Then draw your curtains, and begin the dawn!

           SIR WILLIAM DAVENANT (1606–68)

Folding the Flocks

SHEPHERDS all, and maidens fair,
Fold your flocks up; for the air
'Gins to thicken, and the sun
Already his great course hath run.

See the dew-drops how they kiss
Every little flower that is;
Hanging on their velvet heads,
Like a rope of crystal beads.
See the heavy clouds low falling,
And bright Hesperus down calling
The dead Night from underground;
At whose rising, mists unsound,
Damps and vapours, fly apace,
Hovering o'er the wanton face
Of these pastures, where they come
Striking dead both bud and bloom:
Therefore from such danger lock
Every one his lovèd flock;
And let your dogs lie loose without,
Lest the wolf come as a scout
From the mountain, and ere day
Bear a lamb or kid away;
Or the crafty, thievish fox
Break upon your simple flocks.
To secure yourself from these
Be not too secure in ease;
So shall you good shepherds prove,
And deserve your master's love.
Now, good night! may sweetest slumbers
And soft silence fall in numbers
On your eyelids! so farewell;
—Thus I end my evening's knell.

JOHN FLETCHER (1579–1625)

L'Allegro

HENCE, loathèd Melancholy,
   Of Cerberus and blackest Midnight born
In Stygian cave forlorn
   'Mongst horrid shapes, and shrieks, and sights unholy!
Find out some uncouth cell,
   Where brooding Darkness spreads his jealous wings,
And the night-raven sings;
   There, under ebon shades and low-brow'd rocks,
As ragged as thy locks,
   In dark Cimmerian desert ever dwell.
But come, thou Goddess fair and free,
In heaven yclept Euphrosyne,
And by men heart-easing Mirth;
Whom lovely Venus, at a birth,
With two sister Graces more,
To ivy-crownèd Bacchus bore:
Or whether (as some sager sing)
The frolic wind that breathes the spring,
Zephyr, with Aurora playing,
As he met her once a-Maying,
There, on beds of violets blue,
And fresh-blown roses wash'd in dew,
Fill'd her with thee, a daughter fair,
So buxom, blithe, and debonair.

   Haste thee, Nymph, and bring with thee
Jest, and youthful Jollity,
Quips and Cranks and wanton Wiles,
Nods and Becks and wreathèd Smiles,
Such as hang on Hebe's cheek,

And love to live in dimple sleek;
Sport that wrinkled Care derides,
And Laughter holding both his sides.
Come, and trip it, as you go,
On the light fantastic toe;
And in thy right hand lead with thee
The mountain-nymph, sweet Liberty;
And, if I give thee honour due,
Mirth, admit me of thy crew,
To live with her, and live with thee,
In unreprovèd pleasures free;
To hear the lark begin his flight,
And, singing, startle the dull night,
From his watch-tower in the skies,
Till the dappled dawn doth rise;
Then to come, in spite of sorrow,
And at my window bid good-morrow,
Through the sweet-brier or the vine,
Or the twisted eglantine;
While the cock, with lively din,
Scatters the rear of darkness thin;
And to the stack, or the barn-door,
Stoutly struts his dames before:
Oft list'ning how the hounds and horn
Cheerly rouse the slumb'ring morn,
From the side of some hoar hill,
Through the high wood echoing shrill:
Sometime walking, not unseen,
By hedgerow elms, on hillocks green,
Right against the eastern gate
Where the great Sun begins his state,
Robed in flames and amber light,
The clouds in thousand liveries dight;

[249]

While the ploughman, near at hand,
Whistles o'er the furrow'd land,
And the milkmaid singeth blithe,
And the mower whets his scythe,
And every shepherd tells his tale
Under the hawthorn in the dale.
Straight mine eye hath caught new pleasures,
Whilst the landskip round it measures:
Russet lawns, and fallows grey,
Where the nibbling flocks do stray;
Mountains on whose barren breast
The labouring clouds do often rest;
Meadows trim with daisies pied;
Shallow brooks, and rivers wide;
Towers and battlements it sees
Bosomed high in tufted trees,
Where perhaps some beauty lies,
The cynosure of neighbouring eyes.
Hard by a cottage chimney smokes
From betwixt two aged oaks,
Where Corydon and Thyrsis met
Are at their savoury dinner set
Of herbs and other country messes,
Which the neat-handed Phillis dresses;
And then in haste her bower she leaves,
With Thestylis to bind the sheaves;
Or, if the earlier season lead,
To the tanned haycock in the mead.
Sometimes, with secure delight,
The upland hamlets will invite,
When the merry bells ring round,
And jocund rebecks sound
To many a youth and many a maid

Dancing in the chequer'd shade,
And young and old come forth to play
On a sunshine holiday,
Till the livelong daylight fail:
Then to the spicy nut-brown ale,
With stories told of many a feat,
How Faery Mab the junkets eat.
She was pinch'd and pull'd, she said;
And he, by Friar's lantern led,
Tells how the drudging goblin sweat
To earn his cream-bowl duly set,
When in one night, ere glimpse of morn,
His shadowy flail hath thresh'd the corn
That ten day-labourers could not end;
Then lies him down, the lubber fiend,
And, stretch'd out all the chimney's length,
Basks at the fire his hairy strength;
And crop-full out of doors he flings,
Ere the first cock his matin rings.
Thus done the tales, to bed they creep,
By whispering winds soon lull'd asleep.
Tower'd cities please us then,
And the busy hum of men,
Where throngs of knights and barons bold,
In weeds of peace, high triumphs hold,
With store of ladies, whose bright eyes
Rain influence, and judge the prize
Of wit or arms, while both contend
To win her grace whom all commend.
There let Hymen oft appear
In saffron robe, with taper clear,
And pomp, and feast, and revelry,
With mask, and antique pageantry:

[251]

Such sights as youthful poets dream
On summer eves by haunted stream.
Then to the well-trod stage anon,
If Jonson's learned sock be on,
Or sweetest Shakespeare, Fancy's child,
Warble his native wood-notes wild.

And ever, against eating cares,
Lap me in soft Lydian airs,
Married to immortal verse,
Such as the meeting soul may pierce
In notes, with many a winding bout
Of linkèd sweetness long drawn out,
With wanton heed, and giddy cunning,
The melting voice through mazes running,
Untwisting all the chains that tie
The hidden soul of harmony;
That Orpheus' self may heave his head
From golden slumber on a bed
Of heap'd Elysian flowers, and hear
Such strains as would have won the ear
Of Pluto to have quite set free
His half-regain'd Eurydice.

These delights if thou canst give,
Mirth, with thee I mean to live.

JOHN MILTON (1608–74)

Il Penseroso

HENCE, vain deluding Joys,
    The brood of Folly without father bred !
How little you bested,
    Or fill the fixèd mind with all your toys !

Dwell in some idle brain,
　　And fancies fond with gaudy shapes possess,
As thick and numberless
　　As the gay motes that people the sunbeams,
Or likest hovering dreams,
　　The fickle pensioners of Morpheus' train.

But, hail! thou Goddess sage and holy!
Hail, divinest Melancholy!
Whose saintly visage is too bright
To hit the sense of human sight;
And therefore to our weaker view
O'erlaid with black, staid Wisdom's hue;
Black, but such as in esteem
Prince Memnon's sister might beseem,
Or that starr'd Ethiop queen that strove
To set her beauty's praise above
The Sea-Nymphs, and their powers offended,
Yet thou art higher far descended:
Thee bright-hair'd Vesta long of yore
To solitary Saturn bore;
His daughter she; in Saturn's reign
Such mixture was not held a stain.
Oft in glimmering bowers and glades
He met her, and in secret shades
Of woody Ida's inmost grove,
Whilst yet there was no fear of Jove.
Come, pensive Nun, devout and pure,
Sober, steadfast, and demure,
All in a robe of darkest grain,
Flowing with majestic train,
And sable stole of cypress lawn
Over thy decent shoulders drawn.

Come, but keep thy wonted state,
With even step, and musing gait,
And looks commercing with the skies,
Thy rapt soul sitting in thine eyes:
There, held in holy passion still,
Forget thyself to marble, till
With a sad leaden downward cast
Thou fix them on the earth as fast.
And join with thee calm Peace and Quiet,
Spare Fast, that oft with gods doth diet,
And hears the Muses in a ring
Aye round about Jove's altar sing;
And add to these retirèd Leisure,
That in trim gardens takes his pleasure;
But, first and chiefest, with thee bring
Him that yon soars on golden wing,
Guiding the fiery-wheelèd throne,
The Cherub Contemplation;
And the mute Silence hist along,
'Less Philomel will deign a song,
In her sweetest saddest plight,
Smoothing the rugged brow of Night,
While Cynthia checks her dragon yoke
Gently o'er the accustom'd oak.
Sweet bird, that shunn'st the noise of folly,
Most musical, most melancholy!
Thee, chauntress, oft the woods among
I woo, to hear thy even-song;
And, missing thee, I walk unseen
On the dry smooth-shaven green,
To behold the wandering moon,
Riding near her highest noon,
Like one that had been led astray

Through the heaven's wide pathless way;
And oft, as if her head she bowed,
Stooping through a fleecy cloud.
Oft, on a plat of rising ground,
I hear the far-off curfew sound,
Over some wide-water'd shore,
Swinging slow with sullen roar;
Or, if the air will not permit,
Some still removèd place will fit,
Where glowing embers through the room
Teach light to counterfeit a gloom,
Far from all resort of mirth,
Save the cricket on the hearth,
Or the bellman's drowsy charm
To bless the doors from nightly harm.
Or let my lamp, at midnight hour,
Be seen in some high lonely tower,
Where I may oft outwatch the Bear,
With thrice great Hermes, or unsphere
The spirit of Plato, to unfold
What worlds or what vast regions hold
The immortal mind that hath forsook
Her mansion in this fleshly nook;
And of those demons that are found
In fire, air, flood, or underground,
Whose power hath a true consent
With planet or with element.
Sometime let gorgeous Tragedy
In sceptred pall come sweeping by,
Presenting Thebes, or Pelops' line,
Or the tale of Troy divine,
Or what (though rare) of later age
Ennobled hath the buskin'd stage.

But, O sad Virgin! that thy power
Might raise Musaeus from his bower;
Or bid the soul of Orpheus sing
Such notes as, warbled to the string,
Drew iron tears down Pluto's cheek,
And made Hell grant what love did seek.
Or call up him that left half-told
The story of Cambuscan bold,
Of Camball, and of Algarsife,
And who had Canace to wife,
That own'd the virtuous ring and glass,
And of the wondrous horse of brass
On which the Tartar king did ride;
And if aught else great bards beside
In sage and solemn tunes have sung,
Of tourneys, and of trophies hung,
Of forests, and enchantments drear,
Where more is meant than meets the ear.

Thus, Night, oft see me in thy pale career,
Till civil-suited Morn appear,
Not trick'd and frounced, as she was wont
With the Attic boy to hunt,
But kerchieft in a comely cloud,
While rocking winds are piping loud,
Or usher'd with a shower still,
When the gust hath blown his fill,
Ending on the rustling leaves,
With minute-drops from off the eaves.
And, when the sun begins to fling
His flaring beams, me, Goddess, bring
To archèd walks of twilight groves,
And shadows brown, that Sylvan loves,

Of pine, or monumental oak,
Where the rude axe with heavèd stroke
Was never heard the nymphs to daunt,
Or fright them from their hallow'd haunt.
There, in close covert, by some brook,
Where no profaner eye may look,
Hide me from day's garish eye,
While the bee with honied thigh,
That at her flowery work doth sing,
And the waters murmuring,
With such consort as they keep,
Entice the dewy-feather'd Sleep.
And let some strange mysterious dream
Wave at his wings, in airy stream
Of lively portraiture display'd,
Softly on my eyelids laid;
And, as I wake, sweet music breathe
Above, about, or underneath,
Sent by some Spirit to mortals good,
Or the unseen Genius of the wood.

But let my due feet never fail
To walk the studious cloister's pale,
And love the high embowèd roof,
With antique pillars massy-proof,
And storied windows richly dight,
Casting a dim religious light.
There let the pealing organ blow,
To the full-voiced quire below,
In service high and anthems clear,
As may with sweetness, through mine ear,
Dissolve me into ecstasies,
And bring all Heaven before mine eyes.

And may at last my weary age
Find out the peaceful hermitage,
The hairy gown and mossy cell,
Where I may sit and rightly spell
Of every star that heaven doth shew,
And every herb that sips the dew;
Till old experience do attain
To something like prophetic strain.
    These pleasures, Melancholy, give,
And I with thee will choose to live.

JOHN MILTON

The Hock-Cart, or Harvest-Home

COME, sons of summer, by whose toil
We are the lords of wine and oil;
By whose tough labours and rough hands
We rip up first, then reap our lands.
Crown'd with the ears of corn, now come,
And, to the pipe, sing Harvest Home!
Come forth, my lord, and see the cart
Drest up with all the country art:—
See, here a maukin, there a sheet,
As spotless pure as it is sweet;
The horses, mares, and frisking fillies,
Clad all in linen white as lilies:—
The harvest swains and wenches bound
For joy, to see the hock-cart crown'd.
    About the cart hear how the rout
Of rural younglings raise the shout,
Pressing before, some coming after,
Those with a shout, and these with laughter.

maukin] canvas.

Some bless the cart, some kiss the sheaves,
Some prank them up with oaken leaves;
Some cross the fill-horse, some with great
Devotion stroke the home-borne wheat;
While other rustics, less attent
To prayers than to merriment,
Run after with their breeches rent.

 Well, on, brave boys, to your lord's hearth,
Glitt'ring with fire, where, for your mirth,
Ye shall see first the large and chief
Foundation for your feast, fat beef!
With upper stories, mutton, veal,
And bacon, which makes full the meal;
With sev'ral dishes standing by,
As, here a custard, there a pie,
And here all-tempting frumenty.
And for to make the merry cheer,
If smirking wine be wanting here,
There's that, which drowns all care, stout beer;
Which freely drink to your lord's health,
Then to the plough, the commonwealth,
Next to your flails, your fanes, your fatts;
Then to the maids with wheaten hats;
To the rough sickle, and crook't scythe,
Drink, frolick boys, till all be blythe.
Feed and grow fat, and as ye eat,
Be mindful that the lab'ring neat,
As you, may have their fill of meat;
And know, besides, ye must revoke
The patient ox unto the yoke,
And all go back unto the plough
And harrow, though they're hanged up now.

fill-horse] shaft-horse. fanes] fans. fatts] vats.

And, you must know, your lord's word's true,
Feed him ye must, whose food fills you:
And that this pleasure is like rain,
Not sent ye for to drown your pain,
But for to make it spring again.

                              ROBERT HERRICK (1591–1674)

II

Macpherson's Farewell

FAREWELL, ye dungeons dark and strong,
    The wretch's destinie:
Macpherson's time will not be long
    On yonder gallows tree.

Sae rantingly, sae wantonly,
    Sae dauntingly gaed he;
He played a spring and danced it round,
    Below the gallows tree.

Oh, what is death but parting breath?
    On mony a bloody plain
I've dared his face, and in this place
    I scorn him yet again!

Untie these bands from off my hands,
    And bring to me my sword,
And there's no a man in all Scotland,
    But I'll brave him at a word.

I've lived a life of sturt and strife;
    I die by treacherie:
It burns my heart I must depart
    And not avengèd be.

        spring] dance-measure.   sturt] violence.

Now farewell light, thou sunshine bright,
    And all beneath the sky!
May coward shame distain his name,
    The wretch that dares not die!

ROBERT BURNS (1759–96)

Brignall Banks

O, BRIGNALL banks are wild and fair,
    And Greta woods are green,
And you may gather garlands there,
    Would grace a summer queen:
And as I rode by Dalton Hall,
    Beneath the turrets high,
A Maiden on the castle wall
    Was singing merrily:—

' O, Brignall banks are fresh and fair,
    And Greta woods are green!
I'd rather rove with Edmund there
    Than reign our English Queen.'

' If, Maiden, thou wouldst wend with me
    To leave both tower and town,
Thou first must guess what life lead we,
    That dwell by dale and down:
And if thou canst that riddle read,
    As read full well you may,
Then to the green-wood shalt thou speed
    As blithe as Queen of May.'

Yet sung she, ' Brignall banks are fair,
    And Greta woods are green!
I'd rather rove with Edmund there
    Than reign our English Queen.

'I read you by your bugle horn
    And by your palfrey good,
I read you for a Ranger sworn
    To keep the King's green-wood.'
'A Ranger, Lady, winds his horn,
    And 'tis at peep of light;
His blast is heard at merry morn,
    And mine at dead of night.'

Yet sung she, 'Brignall banks are fair,
    And Greta woods are gay!
I would I were with Edmund there,
    To reign his Queen of May!

'With burnish'd brand and musketoon
    So gallantly you come,
I read you for a bold Dragoon,
    That lists the tuck of drum.'
'I list no more the tuck of drum,
    No more the trumpet hear;
But when the beetle sounds his hum,
    My comrades take the spear.

'And O! though Brignall banks be fair,
    And Greta woods be gay,
Yet mickle must the maiden dare,
    Would reign my Queen of May!

'Maiden! a nameless life I lead,
    A nameless death I'll die;
The fiend whose lantern lights the mead
    Were better mate than I!
And when I'm with my comrades met
    Beneath the green-wood bough,
What once we were we all forget,
    Nor think what we are now.'

Chorus. Yet Brignall banks are fresh and fair,
    And Greta woods are green,
  And you may gather flowers there,
    Would grace a summer queen.

                Sir Walter Scott (1771–1832)

A Wet Sheet and a Flowing Sea

A WET sheet and a flowing sea,
  A wind that follows fast
And fills the white and rustling sail
  And bends the gallant mast;
And bends the gallant mast, my boys,
  While like the eagle free
Away the good ship flies and leaves
  Old England on the lee.

O for a soft and gentle wind!
  I heard a fair one cry;
But give to me the snoring breeze
  And white waves heaving high;
And white waves heaving high, my lads,
  The good ship tight and free—
The world of waters is our home,
  And merry men are we.

There's tempest in yon hornèd moon,
  And lightning in yon cloud;
But hark the music, mariners!
  The wind is piping loud;
The wind is piping loud, my boys,
  The lightning flashes free—
While the hollow oak our palace is,
  Our heritage the sea.

            Allan Cunningham (1784–1842)

Ode to the North-East Wind

WELCOME, wild North-easter!
　　Shame it is to see
Odes to every zephyr;
　　Ne'er a verse to thee.
Welcome, black North-easter!
　　O'er the German foam;
O'er the Danish moorlands,
　　From thy frozen home.
Tired we are of summer,
　　Tired of gaudy glare,
Showers soft and steaming,
　　Hot and breathless air.
Tired of listless dreaming,
　　Through the lazy day:
Jovial wind of winter,
　　Turn us out to play!
Sweep the golden reed-beds;
　　Crisp the lazy dyke;
Hunger into madness
　　Every plunging pike.
Fill the lake with wild-fowl;
　　Fill the marsh with snipe;
While on dreary moorlands
　　Lonely curlew pipe.
Through the black fir-forest
　　Thunder harsh and dry,
Shattering down the snow-flakes
　　Off the curdled sky.
Hark! The brave North-easter!
　　Breast-high lies the scent,

On by holt and headland,
　Over heath and bent.
Chime, ye dappled darlings,
　Through the sleet and snow.
Who can over-ride you?
　Let the horses go!
Chime, ye dappled darlings,
　Down the roaring blast;
You shall see a fox die
　Ere an hour be past.
Go! and rest to-morrow,
　Hunting in your dreams,
While our skates are ringing
　O'er the frozen streams.
Let the luscious South-wind
　Breathe in lovers' sighs,
While the lazy gallants
　Bask in ladies' eyes.
What does he but soften
　Heart alike and pen?
'Tis the hard grey weather
　Breeds hard English men.
What's the soft South-wester?
　'Tis the ladies' breeze,
Bringing home their true loves
　Out of all the seas:
But the black North-easter,
　Through the snowstorm hurled,
Drives our English hearts of oak
　Seaward round the world.
Come, as came our fathers,
　Heralded by thee,

Conquering from the eastward,
   Lords by land and sea.
Come; and strong within us
   Stir the Vikings' blood;
Bracing brain and sinew;
   Blow, thou wind of God!

CHARLES KINGSLEY (1819–75)

The Last Buccaneer

OH England is a pleasant place for them that's rich and
   high,
But England is a cruel place for such poor folks as I;
And such a port for mariners I ne'er shall see again
As the pleasant Isle of Avès, beside the Spanish main.

There were forty craft in Avès that were both swift and
   stout,
All furnished well with small arms and cannons round
   about;
And a thousand men in Avès made laws so fair and free
To choose their valiant captains and obey them loyally.

Thence we sailed against the Spaniard with his hoards of
   plate and gold,
Which he wrung with cruel tortures from Indian folk of
   old;
Likewise the merchant captains, with hearts as hard as
   stone,
Who flog men and keel-haul them, and starve them to
   the bone.

Oh the palms grew high in Avès, and fruits that shone
   like gold,
And the colibris and parrots they were gorgeous to
   behold;

[266]

And the negro maids to Avès from bondage fast did flee,
To welcome gallant sailors, a-sweeping in from sea.

Oh sweet it was in Avès to hear the landward breeze,
A-swing with good tobacco in a net between the trees,
With a negro lass to fan you, while you listened to the
    roar
Of the breakers on the reef outside, that never touched
    the shore.

But Scripture saith, an ending to all fine things must be;
So the King's ships sailed on Avès, and quite put down
    were we.
All day we fought like bulldogs, but they burst the booms
    at night;
And I fled in a piragua, sore wounded, from the fight.

Nine days I floated starving, and a negro lass beside,
Till for all I tried to cheer her, the poor young thing she
    died;
But as I lay a-gasping, a Bristol sail came by,
And brought me home to England here, to beg until I die.

And now I'm old and going—I'm sure I can't tell where;
One comfort is, this world 's so hard, I can't be worse off
    there:
If I might but be a sea-dove, I'd fly across the main,
To the pleasant Isle of Avès, to look at it once again.

                                    CHARLES KINGSLEY

In the Train

As we rush, as we rush in the Train,
    The trees and the houses go wheeling back,
But the starry heavens above the plain
    Come flying on our track.

All the beautiful stars of the sky,
   The silver doves of the forest of Night,
Over the dull earth swarm and fly,
   Companions of our flight.

We will rush ever on without fear;
   Let the goal be far, the flight be fleet!
For we carry the Heavens with us, dear,
   While the Earth slips from our feet!

JAMES THOMSON (1834–82)

The Vagabond

GIVE to me the life I love,
   Let the lave go by me,
Give the jolly heaven above
   And the by-way nigh me.
Bed in the bush with stars to see,
   Bread I dip in the river—
There's the life for a man like me,
   There's the life for ever.

Let the blow fall soon or late,
   Let what will be o'er me:
Give the face of earth around
   And the road before me.
Wealth I seek not, hope nor love,
   Nor a friend to know me;
All I seek, the heaven above,
   And the road below me.

Or let autumn fall on me
   Where afield I linger,
Silencing the bird on tree
   Biting the blue finger.

lave] rest.

[268]

White as meal the frosty field—
    Warm the fireside haven—
Not to autumn will I yield,
    Not to winter even!

Let the blow fall soon or late,
    Let what will be o'er me;
Give the face of earth around,
    And the road before me.
Wealth I ask not, hope nor love,
    Nor a friend to know me;
All I ask, the heaven above,
    And the road below me.

ROBERT LOUIS STEVENSON (1850–94)

Going down Hill on a Bicycle

WITH lifted feet, hands still,
I am poised, and down the hill
Dart, with heedful mind;
The air goes by in a wind.

Swifter and yet more swift,
Till the heart with a mighty lift
Makes the lungs laugh, the throat cry:—
'O bird, see; see, bird, I fly.

'Is this, is this your joy?
O bird, then I, though a boy,
For a golden moment share
Your feathery life in air!'

Say, heart, is there aught like this
In a world that is full of bliss?
'Tis more than skating, bound
Steel-shod to the level ground.

Speed slackens now, I float
Awhile in my airy boat;
Till, when the wheels scarce crawl,
My feet to the treadles fall.

Alas, that the longest hill
Must end in a vale; but still,
Who climbs with toil, wheresoe'er,
Shall find wings waiting there.

HENRY CHARLES BEECHING (1859–1919)

The Song of the Ungirt Runners

WE swing ungirded hips,
And lightened are our eyes,
The rain is on our lips,
We do not run for prize.
We know not whom we trust
Nor whitherward we fare,
But we run because we must
     Through the great wide air.

The waters of the seas
Are troubled as by storm.
The tempest strips the trees
And does not leave them warm.
Does the tearing tempest pause?
Do the tree-tops ask it why?
So we run without a cause
     'Neath the big bare sky.

The rain is on our lips,
We do not run for prize.
But the storm the water whips
And the wave howls to the skies.

[270]

The winds arise and strike it
And scatter it like sand,
And we run because we like it
  Through the broad bright land.

CHARLES HAMILTON SORLEY (1895–1915)

L'Envoi

THERE's a whisper down the field where the year has
    shot her yield
  And the ricks stand grey to the sun,
Singing:—'Over then, come over, for the bee has quit
    the clover
  And your English summer's done.'
    You have heard the beat of the off-shore wind
    And the thresh of the deep-sea rain;
    You have heard the song—how long! how long!
    Pull out on the trail again!

Ha' done with the Tents of Shem, dear lass,
We've seen the seasons through,
And it's time to turn on the old trail, our own trail, the
    out trail,
Pull out, pull out, on the Long Trail—the trail that is
    always new.

It's North you may run to the rime-ring'd sun,
  Or South to the blind Horn's hate;
Or East all the way into Mississippi Bay,
  Or West to the Golden Gate;
Where the blindest bluffs hold good, dear lass,

And the wildest tales are true,
And the men bulk big on the old trail, our own trail, the
    out trail,
And life runs large on the Long Trail—the trail that is
    always new.

The days are sick and cold, and the skies are grey and old,
    And the twice-breathed airs blow damp;
And I'd sell my tired soul for the bucking beam-sea roll
    Of a black Bilbao tramp;
With her load-line over her hatch, dear lass,
And a drunken Dago crew,
And her nose held down on the old trail, our own trail,
    the out trail,
From Cadiz Bar on the Long Trail—the trail that is
    always new.

There be triple ways to take, of the eagle or the snake,
    Or the way of a man with a maid;
But the sweetest way to me is a ship's upon the sea
    In the heel of the North-East Trade.
Can you hear the crash on her bows, dear lass,
And the drum of the racing screw,
As she ships it green on the old trail, our own trail, the
    out trail,
As she lifts and 'scends on the Long Trail—the trail that
    is always new?

See the shaking funnels roar, with the Peter at the fore,
    And the fenders grind and heave,
And the derricks clack and grate, as the tackle hooks the
    crate,
    And the fall-rope whines through the sheave;
It's 'Gang-plank up and in', dear lass,
It's 'Hawsers warp her through!'

And it's 'All clear aft' on the old trail, our own trail,
      the out trail,
We're backing down on the Long Trail—the trail that
      is always new.

O the mutter overside, when the port-fog holds us tied,
    And the sirens hoot their dread!
When foot by foot we creep o'er the hueless, viewless
      deep,
    To the sob of the questing lead:
It's down by the Lower Hope, dear lass,
With the Gunfleet Sands in view,
Till the Mouse swings green on the old trail, our own
      trail, the out trail,
And the Gull Light lifts on the Long Trail—the trail
      that is always new.

O the blazing tropic night, when the wake's a welt of
      light
    That holds the hot sky tame,
And the steady fore-foot snores through the planet-
      powder'd floors
    Where the scared whale flukes in flame!
Her plates are scarr'd by the sun, dear lass,
And her ropes are taunt with the dew,
For we're booming down on the old trail, our own trail,
      the out trail,
We're sagging south on the Long Trail—the trail that is
      always new.

Then home, get her home, where the drunken rollers
      comb,
    And the shouting seas drive by,
And the engines stamp and ring, and the wet bows reel
      and swing,

And the Southern Cross rides high!
Yes, the old lost stars wheel back, dear lass,
That blaze on the velvet blue.
They're all old friends on the old trail, our own trail, the
        out trail,
They're God's own guides on the Long Trail—the trail
        that is always new.

Fly forward, O my heart, from the Foreland to the
        Start—
    We're steaming all too slow,
And it's twenty thousand mile to our little lazy isle
    Where the trumpet-orchids blow!
You have heard the call of the off-shore wind
And the voice of the deep-sea rain;
You have heard the song—how long! how long.
    Pull out on the trail again!

The Lord knows what we may find, dear lass,
And the deuce knows what we may do—
But we're back once more on the old trail, our own trail,
        the out trail,
We're down, hull down on the Long Trail—the trail
        that is always new.

               RUDYARD KIPLING (b. 1865.)

Sea-Fever

I MUST down to the seas again, to the lonely sea and the
    sky,
And all I ask is a tall ship and a star to steer her by,
And the wheel's kick and the wind's song and the white
    sail's shaking,
And a grey mist on the sea's face and a grey dawn breaking.

I must down to the seas again, for the call of the run-
ning tide
Is a wild call and a clear call that may not be denied;
And all I ask is a windy day with the white clouds flying,
And the flung spray and the blown spume, and the sea-
gulls crying.

I must down to the seas again, to the vagrant gipsy life,
To the gull's way and the whale's way where the wind 's
like a whetted knife;
And all I ask is a merry yarn from a laughing fellow-rover,
And quiet sleep and a sweet dream when the long trick 's
over.

                            JOHN MASEFIELD (b. 1877)

Cargoes

QUINQUIREME of Nineveh from distant Ophir,
Rowing home to haven in sunny Palestine,
With a cargo of ivory,
And apes and peacocks,
Sandalwood, cedarwood, and sweet white wine.

Stately Spanish galleon coming from the Isthmus,
Dipping through the Tropics by the palm-green shores,
With a cargo of diamonds,
Emeralds, amethysts,
Topazes, and cinnamon, and gold moidores.

Dirty British coaster with a salt-caked smoke stack,
Butting through the Channel in the mad March days,
With a cargo of Tyne coal,
Road-rail, pig-lead,
Firewood, iron-ware, and cheap tin trays.

                                    JOHN MASEFIELD

Quinquireme] Galley with five banks of oars.

The Old Ships

I HAVE seen old ships sail like swans asleep
Beyond the village which men still call Tyre,
With leaden age o'ercargoed, dipping deep
For Famagusta and the hidden sun
That rings black Cyprus with a lake of fire;
And all those ships were certainly so old
Who knows how oft with squat and noisy gun,
Questing brown slaves or Syrian oranges,
The pirate Genoese
Hell-raked them till they rolled
Blood, water, fruit and corpses up the hold.
But now through friendly seas they softly run,
Painted the mid-sea blue or shore-sea green,
Still patterned with the vine and grapes in gold.

But I have seen,
Pointing her shapely shadows from the dawn
An image tumbled on a rose-swept bay,
A drowsy ship of some yet older day;
And, wonder's breath indrawn,
Thought I—who knows—who knows—but in that same
(Fished up beyond Aeaea, patched up new
—Stern painted brighter blue—)
That talkative, bald-headed seaman came
(Twelve patient comrades sweating at the oar)
From Troy's doom-crimson shore,
And with great lies about his wooden horse
Set the crew laughing, and forgot his course.

Aeaea] Circe's isle.   That . . . seaman] Odysseus.
[276]

It was so old a ship—who knows, who knows?
—And yet so beautiful, I watched in vain
To see the mast burst open with a rose,
And the whole deck put on its leaves again.

JAMES ELROY FLECKER (1884–1915)

III

Hymn to Diana

QUEEN and huntress, chaste and fair,
　　Now the sun is laid to sleep,
Seated in thy silver chair,
　　State in wonted manner keep:
　　　　Hesperus entreats thy light,
　　　　Goddess excellently bright.

Earth, let not thy envious shade
　　Dare itself to interpose;
Cynthia's shining orb was made
　　Heaven to clear when day did close:
　　　　Bless us then with wishèd sight,
　　　　Goddess excellently bright.

Lay thy bow of pearl apart,
　　And thy crystal-shining quiver;
Give unto the flying hart
　　Space to breathe, how short soever:
　　　　Thou that mak'st a day of night—
　　　　Goddess excellently bright.

BEN JONSON (1573–1637)

[277]

To Daffodils

FAIR daffodils, we weep to see
    You haste away so soon;
As yet the early-rising sun
    Has not attain'd his noon.
        Stay, stay
    Until the hasting day
        Has run
    But to the evensong;
And, having pray'd together, we
    Will go with you along.

We have short time to stay, as you,
    We have as short a spring;
As quick a growth to meet decay,
    As you, or anything.
        We die
    As your hours do, and dry
        Away
    Like to the summer's rain;
Or as the pearls of morning's dew,
    Ne'er to be found again.

ROBERT HERRICK (1591–1674)

Daffodils

I WANDER'D lonely as a cloud
    That floats on high o'er vales and hills,
When all at once I saw a crowd,
    A host, of golden daffodils;
Beside the lake, beneath the trees,
Fluttering and dancing in the breeze.

Continuous as the stars that shine
   And twinkle on the Milky Way,
They stretch'd in never-ending line
   Along the margin of a bay:
Ten thousand saw I at a glance,
Tossing their heads in sprightly dance.

The waves beside them danced, but they
   Outdid the sparkling waves in glee:
A poet could not but be gay,
   In such a jocund company:
I gazed—and gazed—but little thought
What wealth the show to me had brought:

For oft, when on my couch I lie
   In vacant or in pensive mood,
They flash upon that inward eye
   Which is the bliss of solitude;
And then my heart with pleasure fills,
And dances with the daffodils.

WILLIAM WORDSWORTH (1770–1850)

To the Cuckoo

HAIL, beauteous stranger of the grove!
   Thou messenger of Spring!
Now Heaven repairs thy rural seat,
   And woods thy welcome ring.

What time the daisy decks the green,
   Thy certain voice we hear:
Hast thou a star to guide thy path,
   Or mark the rolling year?

Delightful visitant! with thee
  I hail the time of flowers,
And hear the sound of music sweet
  From birds among the bowers.

The schoolboy, wand'ring through the wood
  To pull the primrose gay,
Starts, the new voice of Spring to hear,
  And imitates thy lay.

What time the pea puts on the bloom,
  Thou fli'st thy vocal vale,
An annual guest in other lands,
  Another Spring to hail.

Sweet bird! thy bower is ever green,
  Thy sky is ever clear;
Thou hast no sorrow in thy song,
  No Winter in thy year!

O could I fly, I'd fly with thee!
  We'd make, with joyful wing,
Our annual visit o'er the globe,
  Companions of the Spring.

JOHN LOGAN (1748–88)?

To the Cuckoo

O BLITHE New-comer! I have heard,
  I hear thee and rejoice.
O Cuckoo! shall I call thee Bird,
  Or but a wandering Voice?

While I am lying on the grass
  Thy twofold shout I hear;
From hill to hill it seems to pass,
  At once far off, and near.

Though babbling only to the Vale
    Of sunshine and of flowers,
Thou bringest unto me a tale
    Of visionary hours.

Thrice welcome, darling of the Spring!
    Even yet thou art to me
No bird, but an invisible thing,
    A voice, a mystery;

The same whom in my schoolboy days
    I listened to; that Cry
Which made me look a thousand ways
    In bush, and tree, and sky.

To seek thee did I often rove
    Through woods and on the green;
And thou wert still a hope, a love;
    Still longed for, never seen.

And I can listen to thee yet;
    Can lie upon the plain
And listen, till I do beget
    That golden time again.

O blessèd Bird! the earth we pace
    Again appears to be
An unsubstantial, faery place,
    That is fit home for Thee!

WILLIAM WORDSWORTH (1770–1850)

To a Mountain Daisy

On turning one down with the Plough, in April, 1786

WEE modest crimson-tippèd flow'r,
Thou 's met me in an evil hour;
For I maun crush amang the stoure
        Thy slender stem:
To spare thee now is past my pow'r,
        Thou bonnie gem.

Alas! it 's no thy neibor sweet,
The bonnie lark, companion meet,
Bending thee 'mang the dewy weet
        Wi' spreckl'd breast,
When upward springing, blythe to greet
        The purpling east.

Cauld blew the bitter-biting north
Upon thy early humble birth;
Yet cheerfully thou glinted forth
        Amid the storm,
Scarce rear'd above the parent-earth
        Thy tender form.

The flaunting flow'rs our gardens yield
High shelt'ring woods and wa's maun shield,
But thou, beneath the random bield
        O' clod or stane,
Adorns the histie stibble-field,
        Unseen, alane.

stoure] dust.   bield] shelter.   histie] dry.

There, in thy scanty mantle clad,
Thy snawy bosom sun-ward spread,
Thou lifts thy unassuming head
                    In humble guise;
But now the share uptears thy bed,
                    And low thou lies!

ROBERT BURNS (1759–96)

To the Rainbow

TRIUMPHAL arch, that fill'st the sky
    When storms prepare to part,
I ask not proud Philosophy
    To teach me what thou art.

Still seem as to my childhood's sight—
    A midway station given
For happy spirits to alight
    Betwixt the earth and heaven.

Can all that optics teach unfold
    Thy form to please me so
As when I dreamt of gems and gold
    Hid in thy radiant bow?

When Science from Creation's face
    Enchantment's veil withdraws,
What lovely visions yield their place
    To cold material laws!

And yet, fair bow, no fabling dreams,
    But words of the Most High,
Have told why first thy robe of beams
    Was woven in the sky.

[283]

When o'er the green undeluged earth
  Heaven's covenant thou didst shine,
How came the world's grey fathers forth
  To watch thy sacred sign!

And, when its yellow lustre smiled
  O'er mountains yet untrod,
Each mother held aloft her child
  To bless the bow of God.

Methinks, thy jubilee to keep
  The first-made anthem rang
On earth delivered from the deep,
  And the first poet sang.

Nor ever shall the Muse's eye
  Unraptured greet thy beam:
Theme of primaeval prophecy,
  Be still the poet's theme!

The earth to thee her incense yields,
  The lark thy welcome sings,
When glittering in the freshened fields
  The snowy mushroom springs.

How glorious is thy girdle cast
  O'er mountain, tower, and town,
Or mirrored in the ocean vast
  A thousand fathoms down!

As fresh in yon horizon dark,
  As young thy beauties seem,
As when the eagle from the ark
  First sported in thy beam;

For, faithful to its sacred page,
   Heaven still rebuilds thy span,
Nor lets the type grow pale with age
   That first spoke peace to man.

THOMAS CAMPBELL (1777–1844)

The Rainbow

MY heart leaps up when I behold
   A rainbow in the sky:
So was it when my life began;
So is it now I am a man;
So be it when I shall grow old,
   Or let me die!
The Child is father of the Man;
And I could wish my days to be
Bound each to each by natural piety.

WILLIAM WORDSWORTH (1770–1850)

Nightingale and Dove

O NIGHTINGALE! thou surely art
A creature of a ' fiery heart ':—
These notes of thine—they pierce and pierce;
Tumultuous harmony and fierce!
Thou sing'st as if the God of wine
Had helped thee to a Valentine;
A song in mockery and despite
Of shades, and dews, and silent night;
And steady bliss, and all the loves
Now sleeping in these peaceful groves.

[285]

I heard a Stock-dove sing or say
His homely tale, this very day;
His voice was buried among trees,
Yet to be come-at by the breeze:
He did not cease; but cooed—and cooed;
And somewhat pensively he wooed:
He sang of love, with quiet blending,
Slow to begin, and never ending;
Of serious faith, and inward glee;
That was the song—the song for me!

WILLIAM WORDSWORTH

Birds

SURE maybe ye've heard the storm-thrush
  Whistlin' bould in March,
Before there's a primrose peepin' out,
  Or a wee red cone on the larch;
Whistlin' the sun to come out o' the cloud,
  An' the wind to come over the sea,
But for all he can whistle so clear an' loud,
  He's never the bird for me.

Sure maybe ye've seen the song-thrush
  After an April rain
Slip from in-undher the drippin' leaves,
  Wishful to sing again;
An' low wi' love when he's near the nest,
  An' loud from the top of the tree,
But for all he can flutter the heart in your breast,
  He's never the bird for me.

Sure maybe ye've heard the cushadoo
   Callin' his mate in May,
When one sweet thought is the whole of his life,
   An' he tells it the one sweet way.
But my heart is sore at the cushadoo
   Filled wid his own soft glee,
Over an' over his ' me an' you ! '
   He 's never the bird for me.

Sure maybe ye've heard the red-breast
   Singin' his lone on a thorn,
Mindin' himself o' the dear days lost,
   Brave wid his heart forlorn.
The time is in dark November,
   An' no spring hopes has he:
' Remember,' he sings, ' remember ! '
   Ay, *thon* 's the wee bird for me.

MOIRA O'NEILL

To a Skylark

ETHEREAL minstrel ! pilgrim of the sky !
Dost thou despise the earth where cares abound ?
Or, while the wings aspire, are heart and eye
Both with thy nest upon the dewy ground ?
Thy nest which thou canst drop into at will,
Those quivering wings composed, that music still !

To the last point of vision, and beyond,
Mount, daring warbler !—that love-prompted strain,
('Twixt thee and thine a never-failing bond)
Thrills not the less the bosom of the plain :
Yet might'st thou seem, proud privilege ! to sing
All independent of the leafy Spring.

cushadoo] stock-dove.

Leave to the nightingale her shady wood;
A privacy of glorious light is thine;
Whence thou dost pour upon the world a flood
Of harmony, with instinct more divine:
Type of the wise who soar, but never roam;
True to the kindred points of Heaven and Home!

WILLIAM WORDSWORTH (1770–1850)

To a Skylark

HAIL to thee, blithe spirit!
Bird thou never wert—
That from heaven or near it
Pourest thy full heart
In profuse strains of unpremeditated art.

Higher still and higher
From the earth thou springest,
Like a cloud of fire;
The blue deep thou wingest,
And singing still dost soar, and soaring ever singest.

In the golden light'ning
Of the sunken sun,
O'er which clouds are bright'ning,
Thou dost float and run,
Like an unbodied joy whose race is just begun.

The pale purple even
Melts around thy flight;
Like a star of heaven,
In the broad daylight
Thou art unseen, but yet I hear thy shrill delight—

[288]

Keen as are the arrows
    Of that silver sphere
Whose intense lamp narrows
    In the white dawn clear,
Until we hardly see, we feel that it is there.

All the earth and air
    With thy voice is loud,
As, when night is bare,
    From one lonely cloud
The moon rains out her beams, and heaven is overflow'd.

What thou art we know not;
    What is most like thee?
From rainbow clouds there flow not
    Drops so bright to see,
As from thy presence showers a rain of melody:—

Like a poet hidden
    In the light of thought,
Singing hymns unbidden,
    Till the world is wrought
To sympathy with hopes and fears it heeded not :

Like a high-born maiden
    In a palace tower,
Soothing her love-laden
    Soul in secret hour
With music sweet as love, which overflows her bower:

Like a glow-worm golden
    In a dell of dew,
Scattering unbeholden
    Its aërial hue
Among the flowers and grass which screen it from the
    view:

Like a rose embower'd
　　In its own green leaves,
By warm winds deflower'd,
　　Till the scent it gives
Makes faint with too much sweet these heavy-wingèd
　　thieves:

Sound of vernal showers
　　On the twinkling grass,
Rain-awaken'd flowers—
　　All that ever was
Joyous and clear and fresh—thy music doth surpass.

Teach us, sprite or bird,
　　What sweet thoughts are thine:
I have never heard
　　Praise of love or wine
That panted forth a flood of rapture so divine.

Chorus hymeneal,
　　Or triumphal chant,
Match'd with thine would be all
　　But an empty vaunt—
A thing wherein we feel there is some hidden want.

What objects are the fountains
　　Of thy happy strain?
What fields, or waves, or mountains?
　　What shapes of sky or plain?
What love of thine own kind? what ignorance of pain?

With thy clear keen joyance
　　Languor cannot be:
Shadow of annoyance
　　Never came near thee:
Thou lovest, but ne'er knew love's sad satiety.

Waking or asleep,
Thou of death must deem
Things more true and deep
Than we mortals dream,
Or how could thy notes flow in such a crystal stream?

We look before and after,
And pine for what is not:
Our sincerest laughter
With some pain is fraught;
Our sweetest songs are those that tell of saddest thought.

Yet, if we could scorn
Hate and pride and fear,
If we were things born
Not to shed a tear,
I know not how thy joy we ever should come near.

Better than all measures
Of delightful sound,
Better than all treasures
That in books are found,
Thy skill to poet were, thou scorner of the ground!

Teach me half the gladness
That thy brain must know;
Such harmonious madness
From my lips would flow,
The world should listen then, as I am listening now.

PERCY BYSSHE SHELLEY (1792–1822)

The Solitary Reaper

BEHOLD her, single in the field,
   Yon solitary Highland Lass!
Reaping and singing by herself;
   Stop here, or gently pass!
Alone she cuts and binds the grain,
And sings a melancholy strain;
Oh, listen! for the Vale profound
Is overflowing with the sound.

No Nightingale did ever chaunt
   More welcome notes to weary bands
Of travellers in some shady haunt,
   Among Arabian sands:
A voice so thrilling ne'er was heard
In spring-time from the Cuckoo-bird,
Breaking the silence of the seas
Among the farthest Hebrides.

Will no one tell me what she sings?—
   Perhaps the plaintive numbers flow
For old, unhappy, far-off things,
   And battles long ago:
Or is it some more humble lay,
Familiar matter of to-day?
Some natural sorrow, loss, or pain,
That has been, and may be again?

Whate'er the theme, the Maiden sang
   As if her song could have no ending:
I saw her singing at her work,
   And o'er the sickle bending;—

I listen'd, motionless and still;
And, as I mounted up the hill,
The music in my heart I bore,
Long after it was heard no more.

WILLIAM WORDSWORTH (1770–1850)

Arethusa

I

ARETHUSA arose
From her couch of snows
In the Acroceraunian mountains,—
From cloud and from crag,
With many a jag,
Shepherding her bright fountains.
She leapt down the rocks,
With her rainbow locks
Streaming among the streams;—
Her steps paved with green
The downward ravine
Which slopes to the western gleams;
And gliding and springing
She went, ever singing,
In murmurs as soft as sleep;
The Earth seemed to love her,
And Heaven smiled above her,
As she lingered towards the deep.

II

Then Alpheus bold,
On his glacier cold,
With his trident the mountains strook;
And opened a chasm
In the rocks—with the spasm
All Erymanthus shook.

And the black south wind
It unsealed behind
The urns of the silent snow,
And earthquake and thunder
Did rend in sunder
The bars of the springs below.
And the beard and the hair
Of the River-god were
Seen through the torrent's sweep,
As he followed the light
Of the fleet nymph's flight
To the brink of the Dorian deep.

III

'Oh, save me!　Oh, guide me!
And bid the deep hide me,
For he grasps me now by the hair!'
The loud Ocean heard,
To its blue depths stirred,
And divided at her prayer;
And under the water
The Earth's white daughter
Fled like a sunny beam;
Behind her descended
Her billows, unblended
With the brackish Dorian stream:—
Like a gloomy stain
On the emerald main
Alpheus rushed behind,—
As an eagle pursuing
A dove to its ruin
Down the streams of the cloudy wind.

[294]

IV

Under the bowers
Where the Ocean Powers
Sit on their pearlèd thrones;
    Through the coral woods
    Of the weltering floods,
Over heaps of unvalued stones;
    Through the dim beams
    Which amid the streams
Weave a network of coloured light;
    And under the caves,
    Where the shadowy waves
Are as green as the forest's night:—
    Outspeeding the shark,
    And the sword-fish dark,
Under the Ocean's foam,
    And up through the rifts
    Of the mountain clifts
They passed to their Dorian home.

V

And now from their fountains
In Enna's mountains,
Down one vale where the morning basks,
    Like friends once parted
    Grown single-hearted,
They ply their watery tasks.
    At sunrise they leap
    From their cradles steep
In the cave of the shelving hill;
    At noontide they flow
    Through the woods below
And the meadows of asphodel;

[295]

And at night they sleep
In the rocking deep
Beneath the Ortygian shore;—
Like spirits that lie
In the azure sky
When they love but live no more.

PERCY BYSSHE SHELLEY (1792–1822)

The Cloud

I BRING fresh showers for the thirsting flowers,
From the seas and the streams;
I bear light shade for the leaves when laid
In their noonday dreams.
From my wings are shaken the dews that waken
The sweet buds every one,
When rocked to rest on their mother's breast,
As she dances about the sun.
I wield the flail of the lashing hail,
And whiten the green plains under,
And then again I dissolve it in rain,
And laugh as I pass in thunder.

I sift the snow on the mountains below,
And their great pines groan aghast;
And all the night 'tis my pillow white,
While I sleep in the arms of the blast.
Sublime on the towers of my skiey bowers,
Lightning my pilot sits;
In a cavern under is fettered the thunder,
It struggles and howls at fits;
Over earth and ocean, with gentle motion,
This pilot is guiding me,

[296]

Lured by the love of the genii that move
    In the depths of the purple sea;
Over the rills, and the crags, and the hills,
    Over the lakes and the plains,
Wherever he dream, under mountain or stream,
    The Spirit he loves remains;
And I all the while bask in Heaven's blue smile,
    Whilst he is dissolving in rains.

The sanguine Sunrise, with his meteor eyes,
    And his burning plumes outspread,
Leaps on the back of my sailing rack,
    When the morning star shines dead;
As on the jag of a mountain crag,
    Which an earthquake rocks and swings,
An eagle alit one moment may sit
    In the light of its golden wings.
And when Sunset may breathe, from the lit sea beneath,
    Its ardours of rest and of love,
And the crimson pall of eve may fall
    From the depth of Heaven above,
With wings folded I rest, on mine aëry nest,
    As still as a brooding dove.

That orbèd maiden with white fire laden,
    Whom mortals call the Moon,
Glides glimmering o'er my fleece-like floor,
    By the midnight breezes strewn;
And wherever the beat of her unseen feet,
    Which only the angels hear,
May have broken the woof of my tent's thin roof,
    The stars peep behind her and peer;
And I laugh to see them whirl and flee,
    Like a swarm of golden bees,

[297]

When I widen the rent in my wind-built tent,
    Till the calm rivers, lakes, and seas,
Like strips of the sky fallen through me on high,
    Are each paved with the moon and these.

I bind the Sun's throne with a burning zone,
    And the Moon's with a girdle of pearl;
The volcanoes are dim, and the stars reel and swim,
    When the whirlwinds my banner unfurl.
From cape to cape, with a bridge-like shape,
    Over a torrent sea,
Sunbeam-proof, I hang like a roof,—
    The mountains its columns be.
The triumphal arch through which I march
    With hurricane, fire, and snow,
When the Powers of the air are chained to my chair,
    Is the million-coloured bow;
The sphere-fire above its soft colours wove,
    While the moist Earth was laughing below.

I am the daughter of Earth and Water,
    And the nursling of the Sky;
I pass through the pores of the ocean and shores;
    I change, but I cannot die.
For after the rain when with never a stain
    The pavilion of Heaven is bare,
And the winds and sunbeams with their convex gleams
    Build up the blue dome of air,
I silently laugh at my own cenotaph,
    And out of the caverns of rain,
Like a child from the womb, like a ghost from the tomb,
    I arise and unbuild it again.

PERCY BYSSHE SHELLEY

To Autumn

SEASON of mists and mellow fruitfulness!
  Close bosom-friend of the maturing sun;
Conspiring with him how to load and bless
  With fruit the vines that round the thatch-eaves run;
To bend with apples the moss'd cottage-trees,
    And fill all fruit with ripeness to the core;
      To swell the gourd, and plump the hazel shells
    With a sweet kernel; to set budding more,
And still more, later flowers for the bees,
Until they think warm days will never cease,
      For Summer has o'er-brimm'd their clammy cells.

Who hath not seen thee oft amid thy store?
  Sometimes whoever seeks abroad may find
Thee sitting careless on a granary floor,
  Thy hair soft-lifted by the winnowing wind;
Or on a half-reap'd furrow sound asleep,
    Drowsed with the fume of poppies, while thy hook
      Spares the next swath and all its twinèd flowers;
And sometimes like a gleaner thou dost keep
  Steady thy laden head across a brook;
  Or by a cider-press, with patient look,
      Thou watchest the last oozings hours by hours.

Where are the songs of Spring? Aye, where are they?
  Think not of them, thou hast thy music too,—
While barrèd clouds bloom the soft-dying day,
  And touch the stubble-plains with rosy hue;
Then in a wailful choir the small gnats mourn
  Among the river sallows, borne aloft
    Or sinking as the light wind lives or dies;

And full-grown lambs loud bleat from hilly bourn;
  Hedge-crickets sing; and now with treble soft
  The redbreast whistles from a garden-croft;
    And gathering swallows twitter in the skies.

JOHN KEATS (1795–1821)

A Spirit haunts the Year's Last Hours

I

A SPIRIT haunts the year's last hours
Dwelling amid these yellowing bowers:
    To himself he talks;
For at eventide, listening earnestly,
At his work you may hear him sob and sigh
    In the walks;
    Earthward he boweth the heavy stalks
Of the mouldering flowers:
    Heavily hangs the broad sunflower
      Over its grave i' the earth so chilly;
    Heavily hangs the hollyhock,
      Heavily hangs the tiger-lily.

II

The air is damp, and hush'd, and close,
As a sick man's room when he taketh repose
    An hour before death;
My very heart faints and my whole soul grieves
At the moist rich smell of the rotting leaves,
    And the breath
    Of the fading edges of box beneath,
And the year's last rose.

[300]

Heavily hangs the broad sunflower
  Over its grave i' the earth so chilly;
Heavily hangs the hollyhock,
  Heavily hangs the tiger-lily.

      ALFRED, LORD TENNYSON (1809–92)

The Death of the Old Year

FULL knee-deep lies the winter snow,
And the winter winds are wearily sighing:
Toll ye the church-bell sad and slow,
And tread softly and speak low,
For the old year lies a-dying.
    Old year, you must not die;
    You came to us so readily,
    You lived with us so steadily,
    Old year, you shall not die.

He lieth still: he doth not move:
He will not see the dawn of day.
He hath no other life above.
He gave me a friend, and a true true-love,
And the New-year will take 'em away.
    Old year, you must not go;
    So long as you have been with us,
    Such joy as you have seen with us,
    Old year, you shall not go.

He froth'd his bumpers to the brim;
A jollier year we shall not see.
But tho' his eyes are waxing dim,
And tho' his foes speak ill of him,
He was a friend to me.

[301]

Old year, you shall not die;
We did so laugh and cry with you,
I've half a mind to die with you,
Old year, if you must die.

He was full of joke and jest,
But all his merry quips are o'er.
To see him die, across the waste
His son and heir doth ride post-haste,
But he'll be dead before.
    Every one for his own.
    The night is starry and cold, my friend,
    And the New-year blithe and bold, my friend,
    Comes up to take his own.

How hard he breathes! over the snow
I heard just now the crowing cock.
The shadows flicker to and fro:
The cricket chirps: the light burns low:
'Tis nearly twelve o'clock.
    Shake hands, before you die.
    Old year, we'll dearly rue for you:
    What is it we can do for you?
    Speak out before you die.

His face is growing sharp and thin.
Alack! our friend is gone.
Close up his eyes: tie up his chin:
Step from the corpse, and let him in
That standeth there alone,
    And waiteth at the door.
    There's a new foot on the floor, my friend,
    And a new face at the door, my friend,
    A new face at the door.

ALFRED, LORD TENNYSON

Blow, Bugle, blow

THE splendour falls on castle walls
　　And snowy summits old in story:
The long light shakes across the lakes,
　　And the wild cataract leaps in glory.
Blow, bugle, blow, set the wild echoes flying,
Blow, bugle; answer, echoes, dying, dying, dying.

O hark, O hear! how thin and clear,
　　And thinner, clearer, farther going!
O sweet and far from cliff and scar
　　The horns of Elfland faintly blowing!
Blow, let us hear the purple glens replying:
Blow, bugle; answer, echoes, dying, dying, dying.

O love, they die in yon rich sky,
　　They faint on hill or field or river:
Our echoes roll from soul to soul,
　　And grow for ever and for ever.
Blow, bugle, blow, set the wild echoes flying,
And answer, echoes, answer, dying, dying, dying.

ALFRED, LORD TENNYSON

Home-Thoughts, from Abroad

OH, to be in England
Now that April's there,
And whoever wakes in England
Sees, some morning, unaware,
That the lowest boughs and the brushwood sheaf
Round the elm-tree bole are in tiny leaf,
While the chaffinch sings on the orchard bough
In England—now!

And after April, when May follows,
And the whitethroat builds, and all the swallows!
Hark, where my blossom'd pear-tree in the hedge
Leans to the field and scatters on the clover
Blossoms and dewdrops—at the bent spray's edge—
That's the wise thrush; he sings each song twice over,
Lest you should think he never could recapture
The first fine careless rapture!

And though the fields look rough with hoary dew,
All will be gay when noontide wakes anew
The buttercups, the little children's dower
—Far brighter than this gaudy melon-flower!

ROBERT BROWNING (1812–89)

'De Gustibus'

YOUR ghost will walk, you lover of trees,
    (If our loves remain)
      In an English lane,
By a cornfield-side a-flutter with poppies.
Hark, those two in the hazel coppice—
A boy and a girl, if the good fates please,
    Making love, say,—
      The happier they!
Draw yourself up from the light of the moon,
And let them pass, as they will too soon,
    With the beanflowers' boon,
    And the blackbird's tune,
    And May, and June!

ROBERT BROWNING

Are they not all Ministering Spirits?

WE see them not—we cannot hear
  The music of their wing—
Yet know we that they sojourn near,
  The Angels of the spring!

They glide along this lovely ground
  When the first violet grows;
Their graceful hands have just unbound
  The zone of yonder rose.

I gather it for thy dear breast,
  From stain and shadow free:
That which an Angel's touch hath blest
  Is meet, my love, for thee.
                ROBERT STEPHEN HAWKER (1803-75)

What is so Rare as a Day in June?

WHAT is so rare as a day in June?
  Then, if ever, come perfect days;
Then Heaven tries earth if it be in tune,
  And over it softly her warm ear lays;
Whether we look, or whether we listen,
We hear life murmur, or see it glisten;
Every clod feels a stir of might,
  An instinct within it that reaches and towers,
And, groping blindly above it for light,
  Climbs to a soul in grass and flowers;
The flush of life may well be seen
  Thrilling back over hills and valleys;
The cowslip startles in meadows green,
  The buttercup catches the sun in its chalice,
And there's never a leaf nor a blade too mean
  To be some happy creature's palace;

[305]

The little bird sits at his door in the sun,
    A-tilt like a blossom among the leaves,
And lets his illumined being o'errun
    With the deluge of summer it receives;
His mate feels the eggs beneath her wings,
And the heart in her dumb breast flutters and sings;
He sings to the wide world, and she to her nest,—
In the nice ear of Nature which song is the best?

Now is the high-tide of the year,
    And whatever of life hath ebbed away
Comes flooding back with a ripply cheer,
    Into every bare inlet and creek and bay;
Now the heart is so full that a drop overfills it,
We are happy now because God wills it;
No matter how barren the past may have been,
'Tis enough for us now that the leaves are green;
We sit in the warm shade and feel right well
How the sap creeps and the blossoms swell;
We may shut our eyes, but we cannot help knowing
That skies are clear and grass is growing;
The breeze comes whispering in our ear
That dandelions are blossoming near,
    That maize has sprouted, that streams are flowing,
That the river is bluer than the sky,
That the robin is plastering his house hard by;
And if the breeze kept the good news back,
For other couriers we should not lack;
    We could guess it all by yon heifer's lowing,—
And hark! how clear bold chanticleer,
Warmed with the new wine of the year,
    Tells all in his lusty crowing!

JAMES RUSSELL LOWELL (1819–91)

There is a Hill

THERE is a hill beside the silver Thames,
Shady with birch and beech and odorous pine:
And brilliant underfoot with thousand gems
Steeply the thickets to his floods decline.
  Straight trees in every place
  Their thick tops interlace,
And pendant branches trail their foliage fine
  Upon his watery face.

Swift from the sweltering pasturage he flows:
His stream, alert to seek the pleasant shade,
Pictures his gentle purpose, as he goes
Straight to the caverned pool his toil has made.
  His winter floods lay bare
  The stout roots in the air:
His summer streams are cool, when they have played
  Among their fibrous hair.

A rushy island guards the sacred bower,
And hides it from the meadow, where in peace
The lazy cows wrench many a scented flower,
Robbing the golden market of the bees:
  And laden barges float
  By banks of myosote;
And scented flag and golden flower-de-lys
  Delay the loitering boat.

And on this side the island, where the pool
Eddies away, are tangled mass on mass
The water-weeds, that net the fishes cool,
And scarce allow a narrow stream to pass;

myosote] forget-me-not.

[307]

Where spreading crowfoot mars
   The drowning nenuphars,
Waving the tassels of her silken grass
   Below her silver stars.

But in the purple pool there nothing grows,
Not the white water-lily spoked with gold;
Though best she loves the hollows, and well knows
On quiet streams her broad shields to unfold:
   Yet should her roots but try
   Within these deeps to lie,
Not her long reaching stalk could ever hold
   Her waxen head so high.

Sometimes an angler comes, and drops his hook
Within its hidden depths, and 'gainst a tree
Leaning his rod, reads in some pleasant book,
Forgetting soon his pride of fishery;
   And dreams, or falls asleep,
   While curious fishes peep
About his nibbled bait, or scornfully
   Dart off and rise and leap.

And sometimes a slow figure 'neath the trees,
In ancient-fashioned smock, with tottering care
Upon a staff propping his weary knees,
May by the pathway of the forest fare:
   As from a buried day
   Across the mind will stray
Some perishing mute shadow,—and unaware
   He passeth on his way.

nenuphars] water-lilies.

Else, he that wishes solitude is safe,
Whether he bathe at morning in the stream:
Or lead his love there when the hot hours chafe
The meadows, busy with a blurring steam;
    Or watch, as fades the light,
    The gibbous moon grow bright,
Until her magic rays dance in a dream,
    And glorify the night.

Where is this bower beside the silver Thames?
O pool and flowery thickets, hear my vow!
O trees of freshest foliage and straight stems,
No sharer of my secret I allow:
    Lest ere I come the while
    Strange feet your shades defile;
Or lest the burly oarsman turn his prow
    Within your guardian isle.

ROBERT BRIDGES (b. 1844)

London Snow

WHEN men were all asleep the snow came flying,
In large white flakes falling on the city brown,
Stealthily and perpetually settling and loosely lying,
  Hushing the latest traffic of the drowsy town;
Deadening, muffling, stifling its murmurs failing;
Lazily and incessantly floating down and down:
  Silently sifting and veiling road, roof and railing;
Hiding difference, making unevenness even,
Into angles and crevices softly drifting and sailing.
  All night it fell, and when full inches seven
It lay in the depth of its uncompacted lightness,
The clouds blew off from a high and frosty heaven;

And all woke earlier for the unaccustomed brightness
Of the winter dawning, the strange unheavenly glare:
The eye marvelled—marvelled at the dazzling whiteness;
   The ear hearkened to the stillness of the solemn air;
No sound of wheel rumbling nor of foot falling,
And the busy morning cries came thin and spare.

   Then boys I heard, as they went to school, calling,
They gathered up the crystal manna to freeze
Their tongues with tasting, their hands with snowballing;
   Or rioted in a drift, plunging up to the knees;
Or peering up from under the white-mossed wonder,
' O look at the trees!' they cried, ' O look at the trees!'

   With lessened load a few carts creak and blunder,
Following along the white deserted way,
A country company long dispersed asunder:
   When now already the sun, in pale display
Standing by Paul's high dome, spread forth below
His sparkling beams, and awoke the stir of the day.

   For now doors open, and war is waged with the snow;
And trains of sombre men, past tale of number,
Tread long brown paths, as toward their toil they go:
   But even for them awhile no cares encumber
Their minds diverted; the daily word is unspoken,
The daily thoughts of labour and sorrow slumber
At the sight of the beauty that greets them, for the charm
     they have broken.

ROBERT BRIDGES

Rocky Acres

This is a wild land, country of my choice,
    With harsh craggy mountain, moor ample and bare.
Seldom in these acres is heard any voice
    But voice of cold water that runs here and there
    Through rocks and lank heather growing without care.
No mice in the heath run nor no birds cry
For fear of the dark speck that floats in the sky.

He soars and he hovers rocking on his wings,
    He scans his wide parish with a sharp eye,
He catches the trembling of small hidden things,
    He tears them in pieces, dropping from the sky:
    Tenderness and pity the land will deny,
Where life is but nourished from water and rock
A hardy adventure, full of fear and shock.

Time has never journeyed to this lost land,
    Crakeberries and heather bloom out of date,
The rocks jut, the streams flow singing on either hand,
    Careless if the season be early or late
    The skies wander overhead, now blue, now slate:
Winter would be known by his cold cutting snow
If June did not borrow his armour also.

Yet this is my country beloved by me best,
    The first land that rose from Chaos and the Flood,
Nursing no fat valleys for comfort and rest,
    Trampled by no hard hooves, stained with no blood.
    Bold immortal country whose hill tops have stood
Strongholds for the proud gods when on earth they go,
Terror for fat burghers in far plains below.

ROBERT GRAVES (b. 1895)

Inversnaid

THIS darksome burn, horseback brown,
His rollrock highroad roaring down,
In coop and in comb the fleece of his foam
Flutes and low to the lake falls home.

A windpuff-bonnet of fawn-froth
Turns and twindles over the broth
Of a pool so pitchblack, fell-frowning,
It rounds and rounds Despair to drowning.

Degged with dew, dappled with dew
Are the groins of the braes that the brook treads through,
Wiry heathpacks, flitches of fern,
And the beadbonny ash that sits over the burn.

What would the world be, once bereft
Of wet and of wildness?   Let them be left,
O let them be left, wildness and wet;
Long live the weeds and the wilderness yet.

GERARD M. HOPKINS (1844–89)

IV

The Gay Goshawk

'O WELL is me, my gay goshawk,
     That you can speak and flee;
For you can carry a love-letter
     To my true Love from me.'

—'O how can I carry a letter to her?
     Or how should I her know?
I bear a tongue ne'er with her spake,
     And eyes that ne'er her saw.'

twindles : Degged] Invented words, the meaning of which must
be guessed from their sound and context.

—'O well shall ye my true Love ken
    So soon as ye her see:
For of all the flowers of fair England,
    The fairest flower is she.

'And when she goes into the house,
    Sit ye upon the whin;
And sit you there and sing our loves
    As she goes out and in.'

Lord William has written a love-letter,
    Put it under his pinion grey:
And he's awa' to Southern land
    As fast as wings can gae.

And first he sang a low, low note,
    And then he sang a clear;
And aye the o'erword of the sang
    Was 'Your Love can no win here.'

'Feast on, feast on, my maidens all,
    The wine flows you amang;
While I gang to my shot-window
    And hear yon bonnie bird's sang.'

O first he sang a merry sang,
    And then he sang a grave:
And then he peck'd his feathers grey;
    To her the letter gave.

'Have there a letter from Lord William:
    He says, he sent ye three;
He cannot wait your love longer,
    But for your sake he'll die.'

—'I send him the rings from my white fingers,
　　The garlands of my hair;
I send him the heart that's in my breast;
　　What would my love have mair?
And at Mary's kirk in fair Scotland,
　　Ye'll bid him wait for me there.'

She hied her to her father dear
　　As fast as go could she:
'An asking, an asking, my father dear,
　　An asking grant you me!
That if I die in fair England,
　　In Scotland bury me.

'At the first kirk of fair Scotland,
　　You cause the bells be rung;
At the second kirk of fair Scotland,
　　You cause the mass be sung;

'And when ye come to Saint Mary's kirk,
　　Ye'll tarry there till night.'
And so her father pledged his word,
　　And so his promise plight.

The Lady's gone to her chamber
　　As fast as she could fare;
And she has drunk a sleepy draught
　　That she had mix'd with care.

And pale, pale, grew her rosy cheek,
　　And pale and cold was she:—
She seem'd to be as surely dead
　　As any corpse could be.

Then spake her cruel stepminnie,
  'Take ye the burning lead,
And drop a drop on her bosom,
  To try if she be dead.'

They dropp'd the hot lead on her cheek,
  They dropp'd it on·her chin,
They dropp'd it on her bosom white;
  But she spake none again.

Then up arose her seven brethren,
  And hew'd to her a bier;
They hew'd it from the solid oak;
  Laid it o'er with silver clear.

The first Scots kirk that they came to
  They gart the bells be rung;
The next Scots kirk that they came to
  They gart the mass be sung.

But when they came to Saint Mary's kirk,
  There stood spearmen in a row;
And up and started Lord William,
  The chieftain among them a'.

He rent the sheet upon her face
  A little above her chin:
With rosy cheek, and ruby lip,
  She look'd and laugh'd to him.

—'A morsel of your bread, my lord!
  And one glass of your wine!
For I have fasted these three long days
  All for your sake and mine!'

               ANONYMOUS (15th century?)
gart] made.

There is a Lady Sweet and Kind

THERE is a Lady sweet and kind,
Was never face so pleased my mind;
I did but see her passing by,
And yet I love her till I die.

Her gesture, motion, and her smiles,
Her wit, her voice my heart beguiles,
Beguiles my heart, I know not why,
And yet I love her till I die.

Cupid is wingèd and doth range,
Her country so my love doth change:
But change she earth, or change she sky,
Yet will I love her till I die.

ANONYMOUS (*c.* 1600)

To Lucasta, going to the Wars

TELL me not, Sweet, I am unkind,
    That from the nunnery
Of thy chaste breast and quiet mind
    To war and arms I fly.

True, a new mistress now I chase,
    The first foe in the field;
And with a stronger faith embrace
    A sword, a horse, a shield.

Yet this inconstancy is such
    As thou too shalt adore;
I could not love thee, Dear, so much,
    Loved I not Honour more.

RICHARD LOVELACE (1618–58)

To all you Ladies now at Land

To all you ladies now at land
  We men at sea indite;
But first would have you understand
  How hard it is to write;
The Muses now, and Neptune too,
We must implore to write to you—
    With a fa, la, la, la, la.

For though the Muses should prove kind,
  And fill our empty brain,
Yet if rough Neptune rouse the wind
  To wave the azure main,
Our paper, pen, and ink, and we,
Roll up and down our ships at sea—
    With a fa, la, la, la, la.

Then if we write not by each post,
  Think not we are unkind;
Nor yet conclude our ships are lost
  By Dutchmen or by wind:
Our tears we'll send a speedier way,
The tide shall bring them twice a day—
    With a fa, la, la, la, la.

The King with wonder and surprise
  Will swear the seas grow bold,
Because the tides will higher rise
  Than e'er they did of old:
But let him know it is our tears
Bring floods of grief to Whitehall stairs—
    With a fa, la, la, la, la.

Should foggy Opdam chance to know
　　Our sad and dismal story,
The Dutch would scorn so weak a foe,
　　And quit their fort at Goree:
For what resistance can they find
From men who've left their hearts behind?—
　　With a fa, la, la, la, la.

Let wind and weather do its worst,
　　Be you to us but kind;
Let Dutchmen vapour, Spaniards curse,
　　No sorrow we shall find:
'Tis then no matter how things go,
Or who's our friend, or who's our foe—
　　With a fa, la, la, la, la.

To pass our tedious hours away
　　We throw a merry main,
Or else at serious ombre play:
　　But why should we in vain
Each other's ruin thus pursue?
We were undone when we left you—
　　With a fa, la, la, la, la.

But now our fears tempestuous grow
　　And cast our hopes away;
Whilst you, regardless of our woe,
　　Sit careless at a play:
Perhaps permit some happier man
To kiss your hand, or flirt your fan—
　　With a fa, la, la, la, la.

When any mournful tune you hear,
　　That dies in every note
As if it sigh'd with each man's care
　　For being so remote,

Think then how often love we've made
To you, when all those tunes were play'd—
    With a fa, la, la, la, la.

In justice you cannot refuse
    To think of our distress,
When we for hopes of honour lose
    Our certain happiness:
All those designs are but to prove
Ourselves more worthy of your love—
    With a fa, la, la, la, la.

And now we've told you all our loves,
    And likewise all our fears,
In hopes this declaration moves
    Some pity for our tears:
Let's hear of no inconstancy—
We have too much of that at sea—
    With a fa, la, la, la, la.

CHARLES SACKVILLE, EARL OF DORSET (1638–1706)

If Doughty Deeds

IF doughty deeds my lady please,
    Right soon I'll mount my steed;
And strong his arm and fast his seat,
    That bears frae me the meed.
I'll wear thy colours in my cap,
    Thy picture in my heart;
And he that bends not to thine eye
    Shall rue it to his smart!
        Then tell me how to woo thee, Love;
            O tell me how to woo thee!
        For thy dear sake nae care I'll take,
            Tho' ne'er another trow me.

[319]

If gay attire delight thine eye
  I'll dight me in array;
I'll tend thy chamber door all night,
  And squire thee all the day.
If sweetest sounds can win thine ear,
  These sounds I'll strive to catch;
Thy voice I'll steal to woo thysel',
  That voice that nane can match.
    Then tell me how to woo thee, Love . . .

But if fond love thy heart can gain,
  I never broke a vow;
Nae maiden lays her skaith to me,
  I never loved but you.
For you alone I ride the ring,
  For you I wear the blue;
For you alone I strive to sing,
  O tell me how to woo!
    Then tell me how to woo thee, Love;
     O tell me how to woo thee!
    For thy dear sake nae care I'll take,
     Tho' ne'er another trow me.

ROBERT CUNNINGHAME-GRAHAM (1735–97)

The Farewell

IT was a' for our rightfu' King
  We left fair Scotland's strand;
It was a' for our rightfu' King
  We e'er saw Irish land,
    My dear—
  We e'er saw Irish land.

skaith] harm.

Now a' is done that men can do,
   And a' is done in vain;
My love and native land, farewell,
   For I maun cross the main,
        My dear—
   For I maun cross the main.

He turn'd him right and round about
   Upon the Irish shore;
And gae his bridle-reins a shake,
   With, Adieu for evermore,
        My dear—
   With, Adieu for evermore!

The sodger frae the wars returns,
   The sailor frae the main;
But I hae parted frae my love,
   Never to meet again,
        My dear—
   Never to meet again.

When day is gane, and night is come,
   And a' folk bound to sleep,
I think on him that's far awa',
   The lee-lang night, and weep,
        My dear—
   The lee-lang night, and weep.

                                  Robert Burns (1759–96)

A Weary Lot is thine, Fair Maid

'A weary lot is thine, fair maid,
   A weary lot is thine!
To pull the thorn thy brow to braid,
   And press the rue for wine!

        lee-lang] livelong.

A lightsome eye, a soldier's mien,
    A feather of the blue,
A doublet of the Lincoln green,—
    No more of me you knew,
                My love!
    No more of me you knew.

This morn is merry June, I trow,
    The rose is budding fain;
But she shall bloom in winter snow,
    Ere we two meet again.'
He turn'd his charger as he spake,
    Upon the river shore,
He gave his bridle-reins a shake,
    Said, 'Adieu for evermore,
                My love!
    And adieu for evermore.'

                SIR WALTER SCOTT (1771–1832)

My Bonnie Mary

Go fetch to me a pint o' wine,
    An' fill it in a silver tassie;
That I may drink before I go
    A service to my bonnie lassie:
The boat rocks at the pier o' Leith,
    Fu' loud the wind blaws frae the Ferry,
The ship rides by the Berwick-law,
    And I maun leave my bonnie Mary.

The trumpets sound, the banners fly,
    The glittering spears are rankèd ready;
The shouts o' war are heard afar,
    The battle closes thick and bloody;

tassie] cup.

But it's no the roar o' sea or shore
  Wad make me langer wish to tarry;
Nor shout o' war that's heard afar—
  It's leaving thee, my bonnie Mary.

ROBERT BURNS (1759–96)

Lochinvar

O, YOUNG Lochinvar is come out of the west,
Through all the wide Border his steed was the best,
And save his good broad-sword he weapons had none;
He rode all unarmed, and he rode all alone.
So faithful in love, and so dauntless in war,
There never was knight like the young Lochinvar.

He stayed not for brake, and he stopped not for stone,
He swam the Eske river where ford there was none;
But, ere he alighted at Netherby gate,
The bride had consented, the gallant came late:
For a laggard in love, and a dastard in war,
Was to wed the fair Ellen of brave Lochinvar.

So boldly he entered the Netherby hall,
Among bride's-men and kinsmen, and brothers and all:
Then spoke the bride's father, his hand on his sword
(For the poor craven bridegroom said never a word),
'O come ye in peace here, or come ye in war,
Or to dance at our bridal, young Lord Lochinvar?'

'I long wooed your daughter, my suit you denied;—
Love swells like the Solway, but ebbs like its tide—
And now I am come, with this lost love of mine,
To lead but one measure, drink one cup of wine.
There are maidens in Scotland more lovely by far,
That would gladly be bride to the young Lochinvar.'

The bride kissed the goblet; the knight took it up,
He quaffed off the wine, and he threw down the cup,
She looked down to blush, and she looked up to sigh,
With a smile on her lips and a tear in her eye.
He took her soft hand, ere her mother could bar,—
'Now tread we a measure!' said young Lochinvar.

So stately his form, and so lovely her face,
That never a hall such a galliard did grace;
While her mother did fret, and her father did fume,
And the bridegroom stood dangling his bonnet and plume;
And the bride-maidens whispered, ''Twere better by far
To have matched our fair cousin with young Lochinvar.'

One touch to her hand, and one word in her ear,
When they reached the hall-door, and the charger stood
        near;
So light to the croupe the fair lady he swung,
So light to the saddle before her he sprung!
'She is won! we are gone, over bank, bush, and scaur;
They'll have fleet steeds that follow,' quoth young
        Lochinvar.

There was mounting 'mong Græmes of the Netherby
        clan;
Forsters, Fenwicks, and Musgraves, they rode and they
        ran;
There was racing, and chasing, on Cannobie Lee,
But the lost bride of Netherby ne'er did they see.
So daring in love, and so dauntless in war,
Have ye e'er heard of gallant like young Lochinvar?

                    SIR WALTER SCOTT (1771–1832)
                galliard] lively dance.

Jock of Hazeldean

'WHY weep ye by the tide, ladie?
　Why weep ye by the tide?
I'll wed ye to my youngest son,
　And ye sall be his bride:
And ye sall be his bride, ladie,
　Sae comely to be seen'—
But ay she loot the tears down fa'
　For Jock of Hazeldean.

'Now let this wilfu' grief be done,
　And dry that cheek so pale;
Young Frank is chief of Errington,
　And lord of Langley-dale;
His step is first in peaceful ha',
　His sword in battle keen'—
But ay she loot the tears down fa'
　For Jock of Hazeldean.

'A chain of gold ye sall not lack,
　Nor braid to bind your hair,
Nor mettled hound, nor managed hawk,
　Nor palfrey fresh and fair;
And you, the foremost o' them a',
　Shall ride our forest queen'—
But ay she loot the tears down fa'
　For Jock of Hazeldean.

The kirk was deck'd at morning-tide,
　The tapers glimmer'd fair;
The priest and bridegroom wait the bride,
　And dame and knight are there.

loot] let.
[325]

They sought her baith by bower and ha';
   The ladie was not seen!
She's o'er the Border, and awa'
   Wi' Jock of Hazeldean.

SIR WALTER SCOTT

Ruth

SHE stood breast-high amid the corn,
Clasp'd by the golden light of morn,
Like the sweetheart of the sun,
Who many a glowing kiss had won.

On her cheek an autumn flush,
Deeply ripen'd;—such a blush
In the midst of brown was born,
Like red poppies grown with corn.

Round her eyes her tresses fell,
Which were blackest none could tell,
But long lashes veil'd a light,
That had else been all too bright.

And her hat, with shady brim,
Made her tressy forehead dim;
Thus she stood amid the stooks,
Praising God with sweetest looks:—

Sure, I said, Heav'n did not mean,
Where I reap thou shouldst but glean.
Lay thy sheaf adown and come,
Share my harvest and my home.

THOMAS HOOD (1799–1845)

Lady Clare

It was the time when lilies blow,
  And clouds are highest up in air,
Lord Ronald brought a lily-white doe
  To give his cousin, Lady Clare.

I trow they did not part in scorn:
  Lovers long-betroth'd were they:
They two will wed the morrow morn;
  God's blessing on the day!

' He does not love me for my birth,
  Nor for my lands so broad and fair;
He loves me for my own true worth,
  And that is well,' said Lady Clare.

In there came old Alice the nurse,
  Said, ' Who was this that went from thee ? '
' It was my cousin,' said Lady Clare,
  ' To-morrow he weds with me.'

' O God be thank'd ! ' said Alice the nurse,
  ' That all comes round so just and fair:
Lord Ronald is heir of all your lands,
  And you are not the Lady Clare.'

' Are ye out of your mind, my nurse, my nurse ? '
  Said Lady Clare, ' that ye speak so wild ? '
' As God 's above,' said Alice the nurse,
  ' I speak the truth: you are my child.

' The old Earl's daughter died at my breast;
  I speak the truth, as I live by bread !
I buried her like my own sweet child,
  And put my child in her stead.'

'Falsely, falsely, have ye done,
    O mother,' she said, 'if this be true,
To keep the best man under the sun
    So many years from his due.'

'Nay now, my child,' said Alice the nurse,
    'But keep the secret for your life,
And all you have will be Lord Ronald's,
    When you are man and wife.'

'If I'm a beggar born,' she said,
    'I will speak out, for I dare not lie.
Pull off, pull off, the brooch of gold,
    And fling the diamond necklace by.'

'Nay now, my child,' said Alice the nurse,
    'But keep the secret all ye can.'
She said 'Not so: but I will know
    If there be any faith in man.'

'Nay now, what faith?' said Alice the nurse,
    'The man will cleave unto his right.'
'And he shall have it,' the lady replied,
    'Tho' I should die to-night.'

'Yet give one kiss to your mother dear!
    Alas, my child, I sinn'd for thee.'
'O mother, mother, mother,' she said,
    'So strange it seems to me.

'Yet here's a kiss for my mother dear,
    My mother dear, if this be so,
And lay your hand upon my head,
    And bless me, mother, ere I go.'

She clad herself in a russet gown,
　　She was no longer Lady Clare:
She went by dale, and she went by down,
　　With a single rose in her hair.

The lily-white doe Lord Ronald had brought
　　Leapt up from where she lay,
Dropt her head in the maiden's hand,
　　And follow'd her all the way.

Down stept Lord Ronald from his tower:
　　'O Lady Clare, you shame your worth!
Why come you drest like a village maid,
　　That are the flower of the earth?'

'If I come drest like a village maid,
　　I am but as my fortunes are:
I am a beggar born,' she said,
　　'And not the Lady Clare.'

'Play me no tricks,' said Lord Ronald,
　　'For I am yours in word and in deed.
Play me no tricks,' said Lord Ronald,
　　'Your riddle is hard to read.'

O and proudly stood she up!
　　Her heart within her did not fail:
She look'd into Lord Ronald's eyes,
　　And told him all her nurse's tale.

He laugh'd a laugh of merry scorn:
　　He turn'd and kiss'd her where she stood:
'If you are not the heiress born,
　　And I,' said he, 'the next in blood—

'If you are not the heiress born,
    And I,' said he, 'the lawful heir,
We two will wed to-morrow morn,
    And you shall still be Lady Clare.'

ALFRED, LORD TENNYSON (1809–92)

The Day-Dream
The Sleeping Palace

I

THE varying year with blade and sheaf
    Clothes and reclothes the happy plains;
Here rests the sap within the leaf,
    Here stays the blood along the veins.
Faint shadows, vapours lightly curl'd,
    Faint murmurs from the meadows come,
Like hints and echoes of the world
    To spirits folded in the womb.

II

Soft lustre bathes the range of urns
    On every slanting terrace-lawn.
The fountain to his place returns
    Deep in the garden lake withdrawn.
Here droops the banner on the tower,
    On the hall-hearths the festal fires,
The peacock in his laurel bower,
    The parrot in his gilded wires.

III

Roof-haunting martins warm their eggs;
    In these, in those the life is stay'd.
The mantles from the golden pegs
    Droop sleepily: no sound is made,

[330]

Not even of a gnat that sings.
　　More like a picture seemeth all
Than those old portraits of old kings,
　　That watch the sleepers from the wall.

IV

Here sits the Butler with a flask
　　Between his knees, half-drain'd; and there
The wrinkled steward at his task,
　　The maid-of-honour blooming fair:
The page has caught her hand in his:
　　Her lips are sever'd as to speak:
His own are pouted to a kiss:
　　The blush is fix'd upon her cheek.

V

Till all the hundred summers pass,
　　The beams, that thro' the Oriel shine,
Make prisms in every carven glass,
　　And beaker brimm'd with noble wine.
Each baron at the banquet sleeps,
　　Grave faces gather'd in a ring.
His state the king reposing keeps.
　　He must have been a jovial king.

VI

All round a hedge upshoots, and shows
　　At distance like a little wood;
Thorns, ivies, woodbine, mistletoes,
　　And grapes with bunches red as blood;
All creeping plants, a wall of green
　　Close-matted, bur and brake and brier,
And glimpsing over these, just seen,
　　High up, the topmost palace-spire.

VII

When will the hundred summers die,
   And thought and time be born again,
And newer knowledge, drawing nigh,
   Bring truth that sways the soul of men?
Here all things in their place remain,
   As all were order'd, ages since.
Come, Care and Pleasure, Hope and Pain,
   And bring the fated fairy Prince.

The Sleeping Beauty.

I

YEAR after year unto her feet,
   She lying on her couch alone,
Across the purpled coverlet,
   The maiden's jet-black hair has grown,
On either side her trancèd form
   Forth streaming from a braid of pearl:
The slumbrous light is rich and warm,
   And moves not on the rounded curl.

II

The silk star-broider'd coverlid
   Unto her limbs itself doth mould
Languidly ever; and, amid
   Her full black ringlets downward roll'd,
Glows forth each softly-shadow'd arm
   With bracelets of the diamond bright:
Her constant beauty doth inform
   Stillness with love, and day with light.

[332]

III

She sleeps: her breathings are not heard
   In palace chambers far apart.
The fragrant tresses are not stirr'd
   That lie upon her charmèd heart.
She sleeps: on either hand upswells
   The gold-fringed pillow lightly prest:
She sleeps, nor dreams, but ever dwells
   A perfect form in perfect rest.

The Arrival.

I

ALL precious things, discover'd late,
   To those that seek them issue forth;
For love in sequel works with fate,
   And draws the veil from hidden worth.
He travels far from other skies—
   His mantle glitters on the rocks—
A fairy Prince, with joyful eyes,
   And lighter-footed than the fox.

II

The bodies and the bones of those
   That strove in other days to pass,
Are wither'd in the thorny close,
   Or scatter'd blanching on the grass.
He gazes on the silent dead:
   'They perish'd in their daring deeds.'
This proverb flashes thro' his head,
   'The many fail: the one succeeds.'

[333]

III

He comes, scarce knowing what he seeks:
  He breaks the hedge: he enters there:
The colour flies into his cheeks:
  He trusts to light on something fair;
For all his life the charm did talk
  About his path, and hover near
With words of promise in his walk,
  And whisper'd voices at his ear.

IV

More close and close his footsteps wind;
  The Magic Music in his heart
Beats quick and quicker, till he find
  The quiet chamber far apart.
His spirit flutters like a lark,
  He stoops—to kiss her—on his knee.
'Love, if thy tresses be so dark,
  How dark those hidden eyes must be!

The Revival.

I

A TOUCH, a kiss! the charm was snapt.
  There rose a noise of striking clocks,
And feet that ran, and doors that clapt,
  And barking dogs, and crowing cocks;
A fuller light illumined all,
  A breeze thro' all the garden swept,
A sudden hubbub shook the hall,
  And sixty feet the fountain leapt.

[334]

II

The hedge broke in, the banner blew,
　　The butler drank, the steward scrawl'd,
The fire shot up, the martin flew,
　　The parrot scream'd, the peacock squall'd,
The maid and page renew'd their strife,
　　The palace bang'd, and buzz'd and clackt,
And all the long-pent stream of life
　　Dash'd downward in a cataract.

III

And last with these the king awoke,
　　And in his chair himself uprear'd,
And yawn'd, and rubb'd his face, and spoke,
　　' By holy rood, a royal beard!
How say you? we have slept, my lords.
　　My beard has grown into my lap.'
The barons swore, with many words,
　　'Twas but an after-dinner's nap.

IV

' Pardy,' return'd the king, ' but still
　　My joints are something stiff or so.
My lord, and shall we pass the bill
　　I mention'd half an hour ago?'
The chancellor, sedate and vain,
　　In courteous words return'd reply:
But dallied with his golden chain,
　　And, smiling, put the question by.

The Departure.

I

AND on her lover's arm she leant,
  And round her waist she felt it fold,
And far across the hills they went
  In that new world which is the old:
Across the hills, and far away
    Beyond their utmost purple rim,
And deep into the dying day
    The happy princess follow'd him.

II

' I'd sleep another hundred years,
    O love, for such another kiss; '
' O wake for ever, love,' she hears,
    ' O love, 'twas such as this and this.'
And o'er them many a sliding star,
    And many a merry wind was borne,
And, stream'd thro' many a golden bar,
    The twilight melted into morn.

III

' O eyes long laid in happy sleep ! '
    ' O happy sleep, that lightly fled ! '
' O happy kiss, that woke thy sleep ! '
    ' O love, thy kiss would wake the dead ! '
And o'er them many a flowing range
    Of vapour buoy'd the crescent-bark,
And, rapt thro' many a rosy change,
    The twilight died into the dark.

[336]

IV

'A hundred summers! can it be?
    And whither goest thou, tell me where?'
'O seek my father's court with me,
    For there are greater wonders there.'
And o'er the hills, and far away
    Beyond their utmost purple rim,
Beyond the night, across the day,
    Thro' all the world she follow'd him.

ALFRED, LORD TENNYSON

The Beggar Maid

HER arms across her breast she laid;
    She was more fair than words can say:
Bare-footed came the beggar maid
    Before the king Cophetua.
In robe and crown the king stept down,
    To meet and greet her on her way;
'It is no wonder,' said the lords,
    'She is more beautiful than day.'

As shines the moon in clouded skies,
    She in her poor attire was seen:
One praised her ankles, one her eyes,
    One her dark hair and lovesome mien.
So sweet a face, such angel grace,
    In all that land had never been:
Cophetua sware a royal oath:
    'This beggar maid shall be my queen!'

ALFRED, LORD TENNYSON

Lux in Tenebris

SUCH a starved bank of moss
    Till that May-morn,
Blue ran the flash across:
    Violets were born!

Sky—what a scowl of cloud
    Till, near and far,
Ray on ray split the shroud:
    Splendid, a star!

World—how it walled about
    Life with disgrace
Till God's own smile came out:
    That was thy face!

           ROBERT BROWNING (1812–89)

Gifts

GIVE a man a horse he can ride,
    Give a man a boat he can sail;
And his rank and wealth, his strength and health,
    On sea nor shore shall fail.

Give a man a pipe he can smoke,
    Give a man a book he can read;
And his home is bright with a calm delight,
    Though the room be poor indeed.

Give a man a girl he can love,
    As I, O my love, love thee;
And his heart is great with the pulse of Fate,
    At home, on land, on sea.

           JAMES THOMSON (1834–82)

' *When I set out for Lyonnesse* '

WHEN I set out for Lyonnesse,
A hundred miles away,
The rime was on the spray,
And starlight lit my lonesomeness
When I set out for Lyonnesse
A hundred miles away.

What would bechance at Lyonnesse
While I should sojourn there
No prophet durst declare,
Nor did the wisest wizard guess
What would bechance at Lyonnesse
While I should sojourn there.

When I came back from Lyonnesse
With magic in my eyes,
All marked with mute surmise
My radiance rare and fathomless,
When I came back from Lyonnesse
With magic in my eyes!

THOMAS HARDY (b. 1840)

V

Sweet Content

ART thou poor, yet hast thou golden slumbers?
      O sweet content!
Art thou rich, yet is thy mind perplex'd?
      O punishment!
Dost thou laugh to see how fools are vex'd
To add to golden numbers golden numbers?
   O sweet content!   O sweet, O sweet content!
Work apace, apace, apace, apace;
Honest labour bears a lovely face;
Then hey nonny nonny—hey nonny nonny!

Canst drink the waters of the crispèd spring?
      O sweet content!
Swim'st thou in wealth, yet sink'st in thine own tears?
      O punishment!
Then he that patiently want's burden bears,
No burden bears, but is a king, a king!
   O sweet content!   O sweet, O sweet content!
Work apace, apace, apace, apace;
Honest labour bears a lovely face;
Then hey nonny nonny—hey nonny nonny!

THOMAS DEKKER (1570–1641?)

The Character of a Happy Life

How happy is he born and taught
That serveth not another's will;
Whose armour is his honest thought,
And simple truth his utmost skill!

Whose passions not his masters are;
Whose soul is still prepared for death,
Untied unto the world by care
Of public fame or private breath;

Who envies none that chance doth raise,
Nor vice; who never understood
How deepest wounds are given by praise;
Nor rules of state, but rules of good;

Who hath his life from rumours freed;
Whose conscience is his strong retreat;
Whose state can neither flatterers feed,
Nor ruin make oppressors great;

Who God doth late and early pray
More of His grace than gifts to lend;
And entertains the harmless day
With a religious book or friend;

—This man is freed from servile bands
Of hope to rise or fear to fall:
Lord of himself, though not of lands,
And having nothing, yet hath all.

         Sir Henry Wotton (1568–1639)

True Greatness

It is not growing like a tree
     In bulk, doth make men better be;
Or standing long an oak, three hundred year,
To fall a log at last, dry, bald, and sere:
       A lily of a day
       Is fairer far in May,

Although it fall and die that night;
It was the plant and flower of light.
In small proportions we just beauties see;
And in short measures, life may perfect be.

BEN JONSON (1573–1637)

Blow, blow, thou Winter Wind

BLOW, blow, thou winter wind,
Thou art not so unkind
  As man's ingratitude;
Thy tooth is not so keen,
Because thou art not seen,
  Although thy breath be rude.
Heigh ho! sing, heigh ho! unto the green holly:
Most friendship is feigning, most loving mere folly:
  Then heigh ho, the holly!
  This life is most jolly.

Freeze, freeze, thou bitter sky,
That dost not bite so nigh
  As benefits forgot:
Though thou the waters warp,
Thy sting is not so sharp
  As friend remember'd not.
Heigh ho! sing, heigh ho! unto the green holly:
Most friendship is feigning, most loving mere folly:
  Then heigh ho, the holly;
  This life is most jolly.

WILLIAM SHAKESPEARE (1564–1616)

Under the Greenwood Tree

UNDER the greenwood tree,
Who loves to lie with me
And turn his merry note
Unto the sweet bird's throat,
Come hither, come hither, come hither:
Here shall he see
No enemy
But winter and rough weather.

Who doth ambition shun,
And loves to live i' the sun,
Seeking the food he eats,
And pleased with what he gets,
Come hither, come hither, come hither:
Here shall he see
No enemy
But winter and rough weather.

WILLIAM SHAKESPEARE

To Althea, from Prison

WHEN Love with unconfinèd wings
  Hovers within my gates,
And my divine Althea brings
  To whisper at the grates;
When I lie tangled in her hair
  And fetter'd to her eye,
The birds that wanton in the air
  Know no such liberty.

[343]

When flowing cups run swiftly round
　　With no allaying Thames,
Our careless heads with roses bound,
　　Our hearts with loyal flames;
When thirsty grief in wine we steep,
　　When healths and draughts go free—
Fishes that tipple in the deep
　　Know no such liberty.

When, like committed linnets, I
　　With shriller throat shall sing
The sweetness, mercy, majesty,
　　And glories of my King;
When I shall voice aloud how good
　　He is, how great should be,
Enlargèd winds, that curl the flood,
　　Know no such liberty.

Stone walls do not a prison make,
　　Nor iron bars a cage;
Minds innocent and quiet take
　　That for an hermitage;
If I have freedom in my love
　　And in my soul am free,
Angels alone, that soar above,
　　Enjoy such liberty.

RICHARD LOVELACE (1618–58)

The Shepherd's Home

My banks they are furnished with bees,
　　Whose murmur invites one to sleep;
My grottoes are shaded with trees,
　　And my hills are white over with sheep.

[344]

I seldom have met with a loss,
  Such health do my fountains bestow,
My fountains all bordered with moss,
  Where the harebells and violets blow.

Not a pine in the grove is there seen,
  But with tendrils of woodbine is bound;
Not a beech's more beautiful green,
  But a sweet-brier entwines it around.
Not my fields in the prime of the year
  More charms than my cattle unfold;
Not a brook that is limpid and clear,
  But it glitters with fishes of gold.

I have found out a gift for my fair,
  I have found where the wood-pigeons breed;
But let me such plunder forbear,
  She will say 'twas a barbarous deed;
For he ne'er could be true, she averred,
  Who would rob a poor bird of its young;
And I loved her the more when I heard
  Such tenderness fall from her tongue.

WILLIAM SHENSTONE (1714–63)

Bessy and her Spinnin' Wheel

O LEEZE me on my spinnin' wheel,
O leeze me on my rock and reel;
Frae tap to tae that cleeds me bien,
And haps me fiel and warm at e'en!
I'll set me down and sing and spin,
While laigh descends the simmer sun,
Blest wi' content, and milk and meal—
O leeze me on my spinnin' wheel.

leeze me on] blessings on.   bien] comfortably.   fiel] well.

On ilka hand the burnies trot,
And meet below my theekit cot;
The scented birk and hawthorn white
Across the pool their arms unite,
Alike to screen the birdie's nest,
And little fishes' caller rest:
The sun blinks kindly in the biel',
Where blythe I turn my spinnin' wheel.

On lofty aiks the cushats wail,
And Echo cons the doolfu' tale;
The lintwhites in the hazel braes,
Delighted, rival ither's lays:
The craik amang the claver hay,
The paitrick whirrin' o'er the ley,
The swallow jinkin' round my shiel,
Amuse me at my spinnin' wheel.

Wi' sma' to sell, and less to buy,
Aboon distress, below envý,
O wha wad leave this humble state,
For a' the pride of a' the great?
Amid their flaring, idle toys,
Amid their cumbrous, dinsome joys,
Can they the peace and pleasure feel
Of Bessy at her spinnin' wheel?

ROBERT BURNS (1759–96)

biel'] dwelling.   cushats] stock-doves.   lintwhites] linnets.
craik] landrail.   paitrick] partridge.

A Wish

MINE be a cot beside the hill;
  A bee-hive's hum shall soothe my ear;
A willowy brook, that turns a mill,
  With many a fall, shall linger near.

The swallow oft, beneath my thatch,
  Shall twitter near her clay-built nest;
Oft shall the pilgrim lift the latch,
  And share my meal, a welcome guest.

Around my ivied porch shall spring
  Each fragrant flower that drinks the dew;
And Lucy, at her wheel, shall sing,
  In russet gown and apron blue.

The village church beneath the trees,
  Where first our marriage-vows were given,
With merry peals shall swell the breeze,
  And point with taper spire to heaven.

SAMUEL ROGERS (1763–1855)

The Plough

A Landscape in Berkshire.

ABOVE yon sombre swell of land
  Thou see'st the dawn's grave orange hue,
With one pale streak like yellow sand,
  And over that a vein of blue.

The air is cold above the woods;
  All silent is the earth and sky,
Except with his own lonely moods
  The blackbird holds a colloquy.

Over the broad hill creeps a beam,
    Like hope that gilds a good man's brow;
And now ascends the nostril-stream
    Of stalwart horses come to plough.

Ye rigid ploughmen, bear in mind
    Your labour is for future hours:
Advance—spare not—nor look behind—
    Plough deep and straight with all your powers!

RICHARD HENRY HORNE (1803–84)

The Forging of the Anchor

COME, see the *Dolphin's* anchor forged,—'tis at a white
    heat now;
The bellows ceased, the flames decreased,—though on
    the forge's brow
The little flames still fitfully play through the sable mound,
And fitfully you still may see the grim smiths ranking
    round,
All clad in leathern panoply, their broad hands only
    bare,—
Some rest upon their sledges here, some work the windlass
    there.

The windlass strains the tackle chains, the black mound
    heaves below,
And red and deep a hundred veins burst out at every
    throe:
It rises, roars, rends all outright,—O Vulcan, what a
    glow!
'Tis blinding white, 'tis blasting bright,—the high sun
    shines not so!
The high sun sees not, on the earth, such fiery fearful
    show;

The roof-ribs swarth, the candent hearth, the ruddy lurid
  row
Of smiths that stand, an ardent band, like men before the
  foe,
As, quivering through his fleece of flame, the sailing
  monster, slow
Sinks on the anvil,—all about the faces fiery grow.

' Hurrah ! ' they shout, ' leap out,—leap out '; bang,
  bang, the sledges go:
' Hurrah ! ' the jetted lightnings are hissing high and
  low,—
A hailing fount of fire is struck at every squashing blow,
The leathern mail rebounds the hail, the rattling cinders
  strow
The ground around: at every bound the sweltering
  fountains flow,
And thick and loud the swinking crowd at every stroke
  pant ' Ho ! '

Leap out, leap out, my masters; leap out and lay on load !
Let 's forge a goodly anchor,—a bower thick and broad;
For a heart of oak is hanging on every blow, I bode,
And I see the good ship riding all in a perilous road,—
The low reef roaring on her lee,—the roll of ocean poured
From stem to stern, sea after sea; the mainmast by the
  board;
The bulwarks down, the rudder gone, the boats stove at
  the chains !
But courage still, brave mariners, the bower yet remains,
And not an inch to flinch he deigns, save when ye pitch
  sky high;
Then moves his head, as though he said, ' Fear nothing,
  here am I.'

Swing in your strokes in order, let foot and hand keep
   time;
Your blows make music sweeter far than any steeple's
   chime.
But, while you sling your sledges, sing,—and let the
   burden be,
'The anchor is the anvil king, and royal craftsmen we!'

Strike in, strike in,—the sparks begin to dull their rustling
   red;
Our hammers ring with sharper din, our work will soon
   be sped.
Our anchor soon must change his bed of fiery rich array,
For a hammock at the roaring bows, or an oozy couch of
   clay;
Our anchor soon must change the lay of merry craftsmen
   here,
For the yeo-heave-o, and the heave-away, and the sighing
   seaman's cheer;
When, weighing slow, at eve they go,—far, far from love
   and home;
And sobbing sweethearts, in a row, wail o'er the ocean
   foam.

In livid and obdurate gloom he darkens down at last;
A shapely one he is, and strong, as e'er from cat was cast.
O trusted and trustworthy guard, if thou hadst life like me,
What pleasures would thy toils reward beneath the deep
   green sea!
O deep-sea diver, who might then behold such sights as
   thou?
The hoary monster's palaces! methinks what joy 'twere
   now

To go plumb plunging down amid the assembly of the
    whales,
And feel the churned sea round me boil beneath their
    scourging tails!

Then deep in tangle-woods to fight the fierce sea unicorn,
And send him foiled and bellowing back, for all his ivory
    horn;
To leave the subtle sworder-fish of bony blade forlorn;
And for the ghastly-grinning shark to laugh his jaws to
    scorn;
To leap down on the kraken's back, where mid Nor-
    wegian isles
He lies, a lubber anchorage for sudden shallowed miles;
Till snorting, like an under-sea volcano, off he rolls;
Meanwhile to swing, a-buffeting the far astonished shoals
Of his back-browsing ocean-calves; or, haply in a cove,
Shell-strown, and consecrate of old to some Undine's love,
To find the long-haired mermaidens; or, hard by icy
    lands,
To wrestle with the sea-serpent, upon cerulean sands.

O broad-armed fisher of the deep, whose sports can equal
    thine?
The *Dolphin* weighs a thousand tons, that tugs thy cable line;
And night by night, 'tis thy delight, thy glory day by day,
Through sable sea and breaker white, the giant game to
    play.—
But shamer of our little sports! forgive the name I gave,—
A fisher's joy is to destroy,—thine office is to save.
O lodger in the sea-kings' halls, couldst thou but under-
    stand
Whose be the white bones by thy side, or who that dripping
    band,

Slow swaying in the heaving wave, that round about thee
    bend,
With sounds like breakers in a dream blessing their ancient
    friend,—
O, couldst thou know what heroes glide with larger steps
    round thee,
Thine iron side would swell with pride; thou'dst leap
    within the sea.

Give honour to their memories who left the pleasant
    strand,
To shed their blood so freely for the love of Fatherland,—
Who left their chance of quiet age and grassy churchyard
    grave,
So freely, for a restless bed amid the tossing wave,—
O, though our anchor may not be all I have fondly sung,
Honour him for their memory, whose bones he goes
    among!

SIR SAMUEL FERGUSON (1810–86)

Pine Trees

Down through the heart of the dim woods
The laden, jolting wagons come.
Tall pines, chained together,
They carry; stems straight and bare,
Now no more in their own solitudes
With proud heads to rock and hum;
Now at the will of men to fare
Away from their brethren, their forest friends
In the still woods; through wild weather
Alone to endure to the world's ends:
Soon to feel the power of the North
Careering over dark waves' foam;

Soon to exchange for the steady earth
Heaving decks; for the scents of their home,
Honeyed wild-thyme, gorse, and heather,
The sting of the spray, the bitter air.

LAURENCE BINYON (b. 1869)

The Lake Isle of Innisfree

I WILL arise and go now, and go to Innisfree,
And a small cabin build there, of clay and wattles made;
Nine bean rows will I have there, a hive for the honey-bee,
    And live alone in the bee-loud glade.

And I shall have some peace there, for peace comes
        dropping slow,
Dropping from the veils of the morning to where the
        cricket sings;
There midnight's all a glimmer, and noon a purple glow,
    And evening full of the linnet's wings.

I will arise and go now, for always night and day
I hear lake water lapping with low sounds by the shore;
While I stand on the roadway, or on the pavements grey,
    I hear it in the deep heart's core.

WILLIAM BUTLER YEATS (b. 1865)

VI

Boadicea : An Ode

WHEN the British warrior queen,
    Bleeding from the Roman rods,
Sought, with an indignant mien,
    Counsel of her country's gods,

Sage beneath a spreading oak
   Sat the Druid, hoary chief;
Ev'ry burning word he spoke
   Full of rage, and full of grief.

' Princess! if our aged eyes
   Weep upon thy matchless wrongs,
'Tis because resentment ties
   All the terrors of our tongues.

Rome shall perish—write that word
   In the blood that she has spilt;
Perish, hopeless and abhorr'd,
   Deep in ruin as in guilt.

Rome, for empire far renown'd,
   Tramples on a thousand states;
Soon her pride shall kiss the ground—
   Hark! the Gaul is at her gates!

Other Romans shall arise,
   Heedless of a soldier's name;
Sounds, not arms, shall win the prize—
   Harmony the path to fame.

Then the progeny that springs
   From the forests of our land,
Arm'd with thunder, clad with wings,
   Shall a wider world command.

Regions Caesar never knew
   Thy posterity shall sway,
Where his eagles never flew,
   None invincible as they.'

Such the bard's prophetic words,
 Pregnant with celestial fire,
Bending, as he swept the chords
 Of his sweet but awful lyre.

She, with all a monarch's pride,
 Felt them in her bosom glow;
Rush'd to battle, fought, and died;
 Dying, hurl'd them at the foe.

'Ruffians, pitiless as proud,
 Heav'n awards the vengeance due;
Empire is on us bestow'd,
 Shame and ruin wait for you.'

    WILLIAM COWPER (1731–1800)

The Bard

'RUIN seize thee, ruthless King!
 Confusion on thy banners wait,
Tho' fann'd by Conquest's crimson wing
 They mock the air with idle state.
Helm, nor Hauberk's twisted mail,
Nor even thy virtues, Tyrant, shall avail
 To save thy secret soul from nightly fears,
 From Cambria's curse, from Cambria's tears!'
Such were the sounds that o'er the crested pride
 Of the first Edward scatter'd wild dismay,
As down the steep of Snowdon's shaggy side
 He wound with toilsome march his long array.
Stout Glo'ster stood aghast in speechless trance:
—To arms! cried Mortimer, and couch'd his quiv'ring
   lance.

On a rock, whose haughty brow
Frowns o'er old Conway's foaming flood,
    [355]

Robed in the sable garb of woe,
With haggard eyes the Poet stood;
(Loose his beard, and hoary hair
Stream'd, like a meteor, to the troubled air)
And with a Master's hand, and Prophet's fire,
Struck the deep sorrows of his lyre.

'Hark, how each giant-oak, and desert cave,
Sighs to the torrent's awful voice beneath!
O'er thee, oh King! their hundred arms they wave,
Revenge on thee in hoarser murmurs breathe:
Vocal no more, since Cambria's fatal day,
To high-born Hoel's harp, or soft Llewellyn's lay.

'Cold is Cadwallo's tongue,
That hush'd the stormy main:
Brave Urien sleeps upon his craggy bed:
Mountains, ye mourn in vain
Modred, whose magic song
Made huge Plinlimmon bow his cloud-topt head.

On dreary Arvon's shore they lie,
Smear'd with gore, and ghastly pale:
Far, far aloof th' affrighted ravens sail;
The famish'd Eagle screams, and passes by.
Dear lost companions of my tuneful art,
Dear, as the light that visits these sad eyes,
Dear, as the ruddy drops that warm my heart,
Ye died amidst your dying country's cries—
No more I weep. They do not sleep.
On yonder cliffs, a griesly band,
I see them sit, they linger yet,
Avengers of their native land:
With me in dreadful harmony they join,
And weave with bloody hands the tissue of thy line.'

"Weave the warp, and weave the woof,
The winding-sheet of Edward's race.
  Give ample room, and verge enough
The characters of hell to trace.
Mark the year, and mark the night,
When Severn shall re-echo with affright
The shrieks of death, thro' Berkley's roofs that ring,
Shrieks of an agonizing King!
  She-Wolf of France, with unrelenting fangs,
That tear'st the bowels of thy mangled Mate,
  From thee be born, who o'er thy country hangs
The scourge of Heav'n. What Terrors round him wait!
Amazement in his van, with Flight combined,
And Sorrow's faded form, and Solitude behind.

  "Mighty Victor, mighty Lord!
Low on his funeral couch he lies!
  No pitying heart, no eye, afford
A tear to grace his obsequies.
  Is the sable Warrior fled?
Thy son is gone. He rests among the Dead.
The Swarm, that in thy noon-tide beam were born?
Gone to salute the rising Morn.
Fair laughs the Morn, and soft the Zephyr blows,
  While proudly riding o'er the azure realm
In gallant trim the gilded Vessel goes;
  Youth on the prow, and Pleasure at the helm;
Regardless of the sweeping Whirlwind's sway,
That, hush'd in grim repose, expects his evening prey.

  "Fill high the sparkling bowl,
The rich repast prepare,
  Reft of a crown, he yet may share the feast:
Close by the regal chair

[357]

Fell Thirst and Famine scowl
A baleful smile upon their baffled Guest.
Heard ye the din of battle bray,
Lance to lance, and horse to horse?
Long Years of havock urge their destined course,
And thro' the kindred squadrons mow their way.
Ye Towers of Julius, London's lasting shame,
With many a foul and midnight murther fed,
Revere his Consort's faith, his Father's fame,
And spare the meek Usurper's holy head.
Above, below, the rose of snow,
Twined with her blushing foe, we spread:
The bristled Boar in infant-gore
Wallows beneath the thorny shade.
Now, Brothers, bending o'er th' accursed loom
Stamp we our vengeance deep, and ratify his doom.

"Edward, lo! to sudden fate
(Weave we the woof.   The thread is spun.)
Half of thy heart we consecrate.
(The web is wove.   The work is done.)"
'Stay, oh stay! nor thus forlorn
Leave me unbless'd, unpitied, here to mourn:
In yon bright track, that fires the western skies,
They melt, they vanish from my eyes;
But oh! what solemn scenes on Snowdon's height
Descending slow their glitt'ring skirts unroll?
Visions of glory, spare my aching sight,
Ye unborn Ages, crowd not on my soul!
No more our long-lost Arthur we bewail.
All hail, ye genuine Kings, Britannia's Issue, hail!

'Girt with many a Baron bold
Sublime their starry fronts they rear;

And gorgeous Dames, and Statesmen old
In bearded majesty, appear.
In the midst a Form divine!
Her eye proclaims her of the Briton-Line;
Her lion-port, her awe-commanding face,
Attemper'd sweet to virgin-grace.
What strings symphonious tremble in the air,
    What strains of vocal transport round her play!
Hear from the grave, great Taliessin, hear;
    They breathe a soul to animate thy clay.
Bright Rapture calls, and soaring, as she sings,
Waves in the eye of Heav'n her many-coloured wings.

  'The verse adorn again
  Fierce War, and faithful Love,
And Truth severe, by fairy Fiction drest.
  In buskin'd measures move
  Pale Grief, and pleasing Pain,
With Horror, Tyrant of the throbbing breast.
  A Voice, as of the Cherub-Choir,
Gales from blooming Eden bear;
And distant warblings lessen on my ear,
  That lost in long futurity expire.
Fond impious Man, think'st thou yon sanguine cloud,
  Rais'd by thy breath, has quench'd the Orb of day?
To-morrow he repairs the golden flood,
  And warms the nations with redoubled ray.
Enough for me: With joy I see
  The different doom our Fates assign.
Be thine Despair, and scept'red Care;
  To triumph, and to die, are mine.'
He spoke, and headlong from the mountain's height
Deep in the roaring tide he plung'd to endless night.
                    THOMAS GRAY (1716–71)
                [359]

Harlaw

Now haud your tongue, baith wife and carle,
　　And listen, great and sma',
And I will sing of Glenallan's Earl
　　That fought on the red Harlaw.

The cronach 's cried on Bennachie,
　　And doun the Don and a',
And hieland and lawland may mournfu' be
　　For the sair field of Harlaw.

They saddled a hundred milk-white steeds,
　　They hae bridled a hundred black,
With a chafron of steel on each horse's head,
　　And a good knight upon his back.

They hadna ridden a mile, a mile,
　　A mile, but barely ten,
When Donald came branking down the brae
　　Wi' twenty thousand men.

Their tartans they were waving wide,
　　Their glaives were glancing clear,
The pibrochs rung frae side to side,
　　Would deafen ye to hear.

The great Earl in his stirrups stood,
　　That Highland host to see;
'Now here a knight that 's stout and good
　　May prove a jeopardie:

'What would'st thou do, my squire so gay,
　　That rides beside my reyne,
Were ye Glenallan's Earl the day,
　　And I were Roland Cheyne?

cronach] coronach, death-wail.　　　chafron] frontlet.
branking] prancing.

'To turn the rein were sin and shame,
    To fight were wond'rous peril;
What would ye do now, Roland Cheyne,
    Were ye Glenallan's Earl?'

'Were I Glenallan's Earl this tide,
    And ye were Roland Cheyne,
The spur should be in my horse's side,
    And the bridle upon his mane.

'If they hae twenty thousand blades,
    And we twice ten times ten,
Yet they hae but their tartan plaids,
    And we are mail-clad men.

'My horse shall ride through ranks sae rude,
    As through the moorland fern,—
Then ne'er let the gentle Norman blude
    Grow cauld for Highland kerne.'

    .   .   .   .

                SIR WALTER SCOTT (1771–1832)

Agincourt

FAIR stood the wind for France
When we our sails advance,
Nor now to prove our chance
        Longer will tarry;
But putting to the main,
At Caux, the mouth of Seine,
With all his martial train
        Landed King Harry.

kerne] light-armed Highland infantry.

And taking many a fort,
Furnish'd in warlike sort,
Marcheth tow'rds Agincourt
    In happy hour;
Skirmishing day by day
With those that stopped his way,
Where the French gen'ral lay
    With all his power.

Which, in his height of pride,
King Henry to deride,
His ransom to provide
    Unto him sending ;
Which he neglects the while
As from a nation vile,
Yet with an angry smile
    Their fall portending.

And turning to his men,
Quoth our brave Henry then,
'Though they to one be ten
    Be not amazèd:
Yet have we well begun;
Battles so bravely won
Have ever to the sun
    By fame been raisèd.

'And for myself (quoth he)
This my full rest shall be:
England ne'er mourn for me
    Nor more esteem me:
Victor I will remain
Or on this earth lie slain,
Never shall she sustain
    Loss to redeem me.

' Poitiers and Cressy tell,
When most their pride did swell,
Under our swords they fell:
    No less our skill is
Than when our grandsire great,
Claiming the regal seat,
By many a warlike feat
    Lopp'd the French lilies.'

The Duke of York so dread
The eager vaward led;
With the main Henry sped
    Among his henchmen.
Excester had the rear,
A braver man not there;
O Lord, how hot they were
    On the false Frenchmen!

They now to fight are gone,
Armour on armour shone,
Drum now to drum did groan,
    To hear was wonder;
That with the cries they make
The very earth did shake:
Trumpet to trumpet spake,
    Thunder to thunder.

Well it thine age became,
O noble Erpingham,
Which didst the signal aim
    To our hid forces!
When from a meadow by,
Like a storm suddenly
The English archery
    Stuck the French horses.

[363]

With Spanish yew so strong,
Arrows a cloth-yard long
That like to serpents stung,
        Piercing the weather;
None from his fellow starts,
But playing manly parts,
And like true English hearts
        Stuck close together.

When down their bows they threw,
And forth their bilbos drew,
And on the French they flew,
        Not one was tardy;
Arms were from shoulders sent,
Scalps to the teeth were rent,
Down the French peasants went—
        Our men were hardy.

This while our noble king,
His broadsword brandishing,
Down the French host did ding
        As to o'erwhelm it;
And many a deep wound lent,
His arms with blood besprent,
And many a cruel dent
        Bruisèd his helmet.

Gloster, that duke so good,
Next of the royal blood,
For famous England stood
        With his brave brother;
Clarence, in steel so bright,
Though but a maiden knight,
Yet in that furious fight
        Scarce such another.

[364]

Warwick in blood did wade,
Oxford the foe invade,
And cruel slaughter made
  Still as they ran up;
Suffolk his axe did ply,
Beaumont and Willoughby
Bare them right doughtily,
   Ferrers and Fanhope.

Upon Saint Crispin's Day
Fought was this noble fray,
Which fame did not delay
  To England to carry.
O when shall English men
With such acts fill a pen?
Or England breed again
  Such a King Harry?

   MICHAEL DRAYTON (1563?–1631)

Flodden

BLOUNT and Fitz-Eustace rested still
With Lady Clare upon the hill!
On which (for far the day was spent)
The western sunbeams now were bent.
The cry they heard, its meaning knew,
Could plain their distant comrades view:
Sadly to Blount did Eustace say,
'Unworthy office here to stay!
No hope of gilded spurs to-day.
But see! look up—on Flodden bent
The Scottish foe has fired his tent.'

And sudden, as he spoke,
From the sharp ridges of the hill,
All downward to the banks of Till,
    Was wreath'd in sable smoke.
Volum'd and fast, and rolling far,
The cloud envelop'd Scotland's war,
    As down the hill they broke;
Nor martial shout, nor minstrel tone,
Announc'd their march; their tread alone,
At times one warning trumpet blown,
    At times a stifled hum,
Told England, from his mountain-throne
    King James did rushing come.
Scarce could they hear, or see their foes,
Until at weapon-point they close.
They close, in clouds of smoke and dust,
With sword-sway, and with lance's thrust;
    And such a yell was there,
Of sudden and portentous birth,
As if men fought upon the earth,
And fiends in upper air;
O life and death were in the shout,
Recoil and rally, charge and rout,
    And triumph and despair.
Long look'd the anxious squires; their eye
Could in the darkness nought descry.

At length the freshening western blast
Aside the shroud of battle cast;
And, first, the ridge of mingled spears
Above the brightening cloud appears;
And in the smoke the pennons flew,
As in the storm the white sea-mew.

Then mark'd they, dashing broad and far,
The broken billows of the war,
And plumèd crests of chieftains brave,
Floating like foam upon the wave;
    But nought distinct they see:
Wide rag'd the battle on the plain;
Spears shook, and falchions flash'd amain;
Fell England's arrow-flight like rain;
Crests rose, and stoop'd, and rose again,
    Wild and disorderly.
Amid the scene of tumult, high
They saw Lord Marmion's falcon fly:
And stainless Tunstall's banner white,
And Edmund Howard's lion bright,
Still bear them bravely in the fight:
    Although against them come,
Of gallant Gordons many a one,
And many a stubborn Badenoch-man,
And many a rugged Border clan,
    With Huntly, and with Home.

Far on the left, unseen the while,
Stanley broke Lennox and Argyle;
Though there the western mountaineer
Rush'd with bare bosom on the spear,
And flung the feeble targe aside,
And with both hands the broadsword plied.
'Twas vain:—But Fortune, on the right,
With fickle smile, cheer'd Scotland's fight.
Then fell that spotless banner white,
    The Howard's lion fell;
Yet still Lord Marmion's falcon flew
With wavering flight, while fiercer grew
    Around the battle-yell.

The Border slogan rent the sky!
A Home! a Gordon! was the cry:
  Loud were the clanging blows;
Advanc'd, forc'd back, now low, now high,
  The pennon sunk and rose;
As bends the bark's mast in the gale,
When rent are rigging, shrouds, and sail,
  It waver'd 'mid the foes.
No longer Blount the view could bear:
'By Heaven, and all its saints! I swear,
  I will not see it lost!
Fitz-Eustace, you with Lady Clare
May bid your beads, and patter prayer,—
  I gallop to the host.'
And to the fray he rode amain,
Follow'd by all the archer train.
The fiery youth, with desperate charge,
Made, for a space, an opening large,
  The rescued banner rose,
But darkly clos'd the war around,
Like pine-tree, rooted from the ground,
  It sunk among the foes.
Then Eustace mounted too:—yet staid
As loath to leave the helpless maid,
  When, fast as shaft can fly,
Bloodshot his eyes, his nostrils spread,
The loose rein dangling from his head,
Housing and saddle bloody red,
  Lord Marmion's steed rush'd by;
And Eustace, maddening at the sight,
  A look and sign to Clara cast
  To mark he would return in haste,
Then plung'd into the fight.

The scatter'd van of England wheels;

With that, straight up the hill there rode
   Two horsemen drench'd with gore,
And in their arms, a helpless load,
   A wounded knight they bore.
His hand still strain'd the broken brand;
His arms were smear'd with blood and sand:
Dragg'd from among the horses' feet,
With dinted shield, and helmet beat,
The falcon-crest and plumage gone,
Can that be haughty Marmion!
Young Blount his armour did unlace,
And, gazing on his ghastly face,
   Said 'By Saint George, he's gone!
That spear-wound has our master sped,
And see the deep cut on his head!
   Good-night to Marmion.'
'Unnurtur'd Blount! thy brawling cease:
He opes his eyes,' said Eustace; 'peace!'

When, doff'd his casque, he felt free air,
Around 'gan Marmion wildly stare:—
'Where's Harry Blount? Fitz-Eustace where?
Linger ye here, ye hearts of hare!
Redeem my pennon,—charge again!
Cry 'Marmion to the rescue!'—Vain!
Last of my race, on battle-plain
That shout shall ne'er be heard again!
Yet my last thought is England's; fly,
   To Dacre bear my signet-ring:
   Tell him his squadrons up to bring.

[369]

Fitz-Eustace, to Lord Surrey hie;
  Tunstall lies dead upon the field,
  His life-blood stains the spotless shield:
  Edmund is down:—my life is reft;
  The Admiral alone is left.
  Let Stanley charge with spur of fire,—
  With Chester charge, and Lancashire,
  Full upon Scotland's central host,
  Or victory and England's lost.
  Must I bid twice?—hence, varlets! fly!
  Leave Marmion here alone—to die.'
  They parted, and alone he lay;
  Clare drew her from the sight away,
Till pain wrung forth a lowly moan,
And half he murmur'd, ' Is there none,
  Of all my halls have nurst,
Page, squire, or groom, one cup to bring
Of blessèd water from the spring,
  To slake my dying thirst!'

  .   .   .   .

The war, that for a space did fail,
Now trebly thundering swell'd the gale,
  And—STANLEY! was the cry;
A light on Marmion's visage spread,
  And fired his glazing eye:
With dying hand, above his head,
He shook the fragment of his blade,
  And shouted ' Victory!
Charge, Chester, charge!   On, Stanley, on!'
Were the last words of Marmion.

By this, though deep the evening fell,
Still rose the battle's deadly swell,

For still the Scots, around their King,
Unbroken, fought in desperate ring.
Where's now their victor vaward wing,
    Where Huntly, and where Home?—
O, for a blast of that dread horn,
On Fontarabian echoes borne,
    That to King Charles did come,
When Rowland brave, and Olivier,
And every paladin and peer,
    On Roncesvalles died!
Such blast might warn them, not in vain,
To quit the plunder of the slain,
And turn the doubtful day again,
    While yet on Flodden side,
Afar, the Royal Standard flies,
And round it toils, and bleeds, and dies,
    Our Caledonian pride!

      .   .   .   .   .

'O, Lady,' cried the Monk, 'away!'
    And plac'd her on her steed,
And led her to the chapel fair,
    Of Tilmouth upon Tweed.

      .   .   .   .   .   .

But as they left the dark'ning heath,
More desperate grew the strife of death.
The English shafts in volleys hail'd,
In headlong charge their horse assail'd;
Front, flank, and rear, the squadrons sweep
To break the Scottish circle deep,
    That fought around their King.
But yet, though thick the shafts as snow,
Though charging knights like whirlwinds go,

Though bill-men ply the ghastly blow,
　　Unbroken was the ring;
The stubborn spear-men still made good
Their dark impenetrable wood,
Each stepping where his comrade stood,
　　The instant that he fell.
No thought was there of dastard flight;
Link'd in the serried phalanx tight,
Groom fought like noble, squire like knight,
　　As fearlessly and well;
Till utter darkness closed her wing
O'er their thin host and wounded King.

Then skilful Surrey's sage commands
Led back from strife his shatter'd bands;
　　And from the charge they drew,
As mountain-waves, from wasted lands,
　　Sweep back to ocean blue.
Then did their loss his foemen know;
Their King, their Lords, their mightiest low,
They melted from the field as snow,
When streams are swoln and south winds blow,
　　Dissolves in silent dew.
Tweed's echoes heard the ceaseless plash,
　　While many a broken band,
Disorder'd, through her currents dash
　　To gain the Scottish land;
To town and tower, to down and dale,
To tell red Flodden's dismal tale,
And raise the universal wail.
Tradition, legend, tune, and song,
Shall many an age that wail prolong:
Still from the sire the son shall hear
Of the stern strife, and carnage drear,

Of Flodden's fatal field,
Where shiver'd was fair Scotland's spear,
And broken was her shield!

Sir Walter Scott (1771–1832)

The Armada

Attend, all ye who list to hear our noble England's praise;
I tell of the thrice-famous deeds she wrought in ancient
days,
When that great fleet invincible against her bore in vain
The richest spoils of Mexico, the stoutest hearts of Spain.

It was about the lovely close of a warm summer day,
There came a gallant merchant-ship full sail to Plymouth
Bay;
Her crew had seen Castile's black fleet, beyond Aurigny's
Isle,
At earliest twilight, on the waves lie heaving many a mile.
At sunrise she escaped their van, by God's especial grace:
And the tall Pinta, till the noon, had held her close in
chase.
Forthwith a guard at every gun was placed along the wall;
The beacon blazed upon the roof of Edgecumbe's lofty
hall;
Many a light fishing bark put out to pry along the coast,
And with loose rein and bloody spur rode inland many a
post.
With his white hair unbonneted, the stout old sheriff
comes;
Behind him march the halberdiers; before him sound the
drums;

His yeomen round the market cross make clear an ample
      space;

For there behoves him to set up the standard of Her Grace.

And haughtily the trumpets peal and gaily dance the bells,

As slow upon the labouring wind the royal blazon swells.

Look how the Lion of the sea lifts up his ancient crown,

And underneath his deadly paw treads the gay lilies down.

So stalked he when he turned to flight, on that famed
      Picard field,

Bohemia's plume, and Genoa's bow, and Caesar's eagle
      shield.

So glared he when at Agincourt in wrath he turned to bay,

And crushed and torn beneath his claws the princely hunters
      lay.

Ho! strike the flagstaff deep, Sir Knight: ho! scatter
      flowers, fair maids:

Ho! gunners, fire a loud salute: ho! gallants, draw your
      blades:

Thou sun, shine on her joyously; ye breezes, waft her wide;

Our glorious SEMPER EADEM, the banner of our pride.

The freshening breeze of eve unfurled that banner's massy
      fold;

The parting gleam of sunshine kissed that haughty scroll
      of gold;

Night sank upon the dusky beach, and on the purple sea,

Such night in England ne'er had been, nor e'er again shall be.

From Eddystone to Berwick bounds, from Lynn to
      Milford Bay,

That time of slumber was as bright and busy as the day;

For swift to east and swift to west the ghastly war-flame
      spread,

High on St. Michael's Mount it shone; it shone on
      Beachy Head.

Far on the deep the Spaniards saw, along each southern shire,
Cape beyond cape, in endless range, those twinkling points
of fire.
The fisher left his skiff to rock on Tamar's glittering
waves:
The rugged miners poured to war from Mendip's sunless
caves:
O'er Longleat's towers, o'er Cranbourne's oaks, the fiery
herald flew:
He roused the shepherds of Stonehenge, the rangers of
Beaulieu.
Right sharp and quick the bells all night rang out from
Bristol town,
And ere the day three hundred horse had met on Clifton
Down;
The sentinel on Whitehall gate looked forth into the night,
And saw o'erhanging Richmond Hill the streak of blood-
red light;
Then bugle's note and cannon's roar the death-like silence
broke,
And with one start and with one cry, the royal city woke.
At once on all her stately gates arose the answering fires;
At once the wild alarum clashed from all her reeling spires;
From all the batteries of the Tower pealed loud the voice
of fear;
And all the thousand masts of Thames sent back a louder
cheer;
And from the furthest wards was heard the rush of hurry-
ing feet,
And the broad streams of pikes and flags rushed down each
roaring street;
And broader still became the blaze, and louder still the din,
As fast from every village round the horse came spurring in:

And eastward straight from wild Blackheath the warlike
 errand went,

And roused in many an ancient hall the gallant squires of
 Kent.

Southward from Surrey's pleasant hills flew those bright
 couriers forth;

High on bleak Hampstead's swarthy moor they started for
 the north;

And on, and on, without a pause, untired they bounded
 still:

All night from tower to tower they sprang: they sprang
 from hill to hill:

Till the proud Peak unfurled the flag o'er Darwin's rocky
 dales,

Till like volcanoes flared to heaven the stormy hills of
 Wales.

Till twelve fair counties saw the blaze on Malvern's lonely
 height,

Till streamed in crimson on the wind the Wrekin's crest
 of light,

Till broad and fierce the star came forth on Ely's stately
 fane,

And tower and hamlet rose in arms o'er all the boundless
 plain;

Till Belvoir's lordly terraces the sign to Lincoln sent,

And Lincoln sped the message on o'er the wide vale of
 Trent;

Till Skiddaw saw the fire that burned on Gaunt's em-
 battled pile,

And the red glare on Skiddaw roused the burghers of
 Carlisle.

LORD MACAULAY (1800–59)

[376]

Drake's Drum

DRAKE he's in his hammock an' a thousand mile away,
  (Capten, art tha sleepin' there below?)
Slung atween the round shot in Nombre Dios Bay,
  An' dreamin' arl the time o' Plymouth Hoe.
Yarnder lumes the Island, yarnder lie the ships,
  Wi' sailor lads a-dancin' heel-an'-toe,
An' the shore-lights flashin', an' the night-tide dashin',
  He sees et arl so plainly as he saw et long ago.

Drake he was a Devon man, an' ruled the Devon seas,
  (Capten, art tha sleepin' there below?)
Rovin' tho' his death fell, he went wi' heart at ease,
  An' dreamin' arl the time o' Plymouth Hoe.
'Take my drum to England, hang et by the shore,
  Strike et when your powder's runnin' low;
If the Dons sight Devon, I'll quit the port o' Heaven,
  An' drum them up the Channel as we drummed them
    long ago.'

Drake he's in his hammock till the great Armadas come,
  (Capten, art tha sleepin' there below?)
Slung atween the round shot, listenin' for the drum,
  An' dreamin' arl the time o' Plymouth Hoe.
Call him on the deep sea, call him up the Sound,
  Call him when ye sail to meet the foe;
Where the old trade's plyin' an' the old flag flyin'
  They shall find him ware an' wakin', as they found
    him long ago!

SIR HENRY NEWBOLT (b. 1862)

[377]

The Landing of the Pilgrim Fathers in New England

THE breaking waves dashed high
  On a stern and rock-bound coast,
And the woods against a stormy sky
  Their giant branches tossed.

And the heavy night hung dark
  The hills and waters o'er,
When a band of exiles moored their bark
  On the wild New England shore.

Not as the conqueror comes,
  They, the true-hearted, came;
Not with the roll of the stirring drums,
  And the trumpet that sings of fame.

Not as the flying come,
  In silence and in fear:—
They shook the depths of the desert gloom
  With their hymns of lofty cheer.

Amidst the storm they sang,
  And the stars heard, and the sea:
And the sounding aisles of the dim woods rang
  To the anthem of the free!

The ocean eagle soared
  From his nest by the white wave's foam:
And the rocking pines of the forest roared,—
  This was their welcome home!

There were men with hoary hair
  Amidst that pilgrim band:—
Why had *they* come to wither there,
  Away from their childhood's land?

There was woman's fearless eye,
  Lit by her deep love's truth;
There was manhood's brow serenely high,
  And the fiery heart of youth.

What sought they thus afar?
  Bright jewels of the mine?
The wealth of seas, the spoils of war?
  They sought a faith's pure shrine!

Aye, call it holy ground,
  The soil where first they trod:
They have left unstained what there they found,—
  Freedom to worship God.

FELICIA DOROTHEA HEMANS (1793–1835)

The Battle of Naseby

'OH! wherefore come ye forth, in triumph from the
    North,
  With your hands, and your feet, and your raiment all
      red?
And wherefore doth your rout send forth a joyous shout?
  And whence be the grapes of the wine-press which ye
      tread?'

'Oh evil was the root, and bitter was the fruit,
  And crimson was the juice of the vintage that we trod;
For we trampled on the throng of the haughty and the
      strong,
  Who sate in the high places, and slew the saints of God.

It was about the noon of a glorious day of June
  That we saw their banners dance and their cuirasses
      shine,

[379]

And the Man of Blood was there, with his long essencèd
        hair,
    And Astley, and Sir Marmaduke, and Rupert of the
        Rhine.

Like a servant of the Lord, with his Bible and his sword,
    The General rode along us to form us to the fight,
When a murmuring sound broke out, and swell'd into a
        shout,
    Among the godless horsemen upon the tyrant's right.

And hark! like the roar of the billows on the shore,
    The cry of battle rises along their charging line!
For God! for the Cause! for the Church! for the Laws!
    For Charles King of England and Rupert of the Rhine!

The furious German comes, with his clarions and his
        drums,
    His bravoes of Alsatia, and pages of Whitehall;
They are bursting on our flanks. Grasp your pikes, close
        your ranks;
    For Rupert never comes but to conquer or to fall.

They are here! They rush on! We are broken! We are
        gone!
    Our left is borne before them like stubble on the blast.
O Lord, put forth thy might! O Lord, defend the right!
    Stand back to back, in God's name, and fight it to the
        last.

Stout Skippon hath a wound; the centre hath given
        ground:
    Hark! hark!—What means the trampling of horsemen
        on our rear?
Whose banner do I see, boys? 'Tis he, thank God, 'tis he,
        boys,
    Bear up another minute: brave Oliver is here.

Their heads all stooping low, their points all in a row,
  Like a whirlwind on the trees, like a deluge on the dykes,
Our cuirassiers have burst on the ranks of the Accurst,
  And at a shock have scattered the forest of his pikes.

Fast, fast, the gallants ride, in some safe nook to hide
  Their coward heads, predestined to rot on Temple Bar;
And he—he turns, he flies:—shame on those cruel eyes
  That bore to look on torture, and dare not look on war.

Ho! comrades, scour the plain; and, ere ye strip the slain,
  First give another stab to make your search secure,
Then shake from sleeves and pockets their broad-pieces
      and lockets,
  The tokens of the wanton, the plunder of the poor.

Fools! your doublets shone with gold, and your hearts
      were gay and bold,
  When you kissed your lily hands to your lemans to-day;
And to-morrow shall the fox, from her chambers in the
      rocks,
  Lead forth her tawny cubs to howl above the prey.

Where be your tongues that late mocked at heaven and
      hell and fate,
  And the fingers that once were so busy with your
      blades,
Your perfum'd satin clothes, your catches and your oaths,
  Your stage-plays and your sonnets, your diamonds and
      your spades?

Down, down, for ever down with the mitre and the crown,
  With the Belial of the Court and the Mammon of the
      Pope;
There is woe in Oxford Halls: there is wail in Durham's
      Stalls:
  The Jesuit smites his bosom: the Bishop rends his cope.

And She of the seven hills shall mourn her children's ills,
    And tremble when she thinks on the edge of England's
        sword;
And the Kings of earth in fear shall shudder when they
        hear
    What the hand of God hath wrought for the Houses
        and the Word.'

                LORD MACAULAY (1800–59)

The Battle of the Baltic

OF Nelson and the North
Sing the glorious day's renown,
When to battle fierce came forth
All the might of Denmark's crown,
And her arms along the deep proudly shone,—
By each gun the lighted brand
In a bold determined hand;
And the Prince of all the land
Led them on.

Like leviathans afloat
Lay their bulwarks on the brine,
While the sign of battle flew
On the lofty British line:
It was ten of April morn by the chime:
As they drifted on their path
There was silence deep as death,
And the boldest held his breath
For a time.

But the might of England flushed
To anticipate the scene;
And her van the fleeter rushed
O'er the deadly space between.

'Hearts of oak!' our captain cried; when each gun
From its adamantine lips
Spread a death-shade round the ships,
Like the hurricane eclipse
Of the sun.

Again! again! again!
And the havoc did not slack,
Till a feeble cheer the Dane
To our cheering sent us back:
Their shots along the deep slowly boom;
Then ceased—and all is wail
As they strike the shattered sail,
Or, in conflagration pale,
Light the gloom.

Out spoke the victor then,
As he hailed them o'er the wave,
'Ye are brothers! ye are men!
And we conquer but to save;
So peace instead of death let us bring:
But yield, proud foe, thy fleet
With the crews at England's feet,
And make submission meet
To our King.'

Then Denmark blessed our chief
That he gave her wounds repose;
And the sounds of joy and grief
From her people wildly rose,
As death withdrew his shades from the day;
While the sun looked smiling bright
O'er a wild and woeful sight,
Where the fires of funeral light
Died away.

Now joy, Old England, raise
For the tidings of thy might,
By the festal cities' blaze,
While the wine-cup shines in light;
And yet, amidst that joy and uproar,
Let us think of them that sleep,
Full many a fathom deep,
By thy wild and stormy steep,
Elsinore!

Brave hearts! to Britain's pride
Once so faithful and so true,
On the deck of fame that died
With the gallant good Riou—
Soft sigh the winds of Heaven o'er their grave!
While the billow mournful rolls
And the mermaid's song condoles,
Singing glory to the souls
Of the brave!

THOMAS CAMPBELL (1777–1844)

Hohenlinden

On Linden, when the sun was low,
All bloodless lay the untrodden snow,
And dark as winter was the flow
    Of Iser, rolling rapidly.

But Linden saw another sight
When the drum beat at dead of night,
Commanding fires of death to light
    The darkness of her scenery.

By torch and trumpet fast arrayed,
Each horseman drew his battle blade,
And furious every charger neighed
　　　To join the dreadful revelry.

Then shook the hills with thunder riven,
Then rushed the steed to battle driven,
And louder than the bolts of heaven
　　　Far flashed the red artillery.

But redder yet that light shall glow
On Linden's hills of stainèd snow,
And bloodier yet the torrent flow
　　　Of Iser, rolling rapidly.

'Tis morn, but scarce yon level sun
Can pierce the war-clouds, rolling dun,
Where furious Frank and fiery Hun
　　　Shout in their sulphurous canopy.

The combat deepens. On, ye brave,
Who rush to glory, or the grave!
Wave, Munich! all thy banners wave,
　　　And charge with all thy chivalry!

Few, few shall part where many meet!
The snow shall be their winding-sheet,
And every turf beneath their feet
　　　Shall be a soldier's sepulchre.

THOMAS CAMPBELL

The Burial of Sir John Moore after Corunna

NOT a drum was heard, not a funeral note,
　　As his corse to the rampart we hurried;
Not a soldier discharged his farewell shot
　　O'er the grave where our hero we buried.

We buried him darkly at dead of night,
  The sods with our bayonets turning,
By the struggling moonbeam's misty light
  And the lanthorn dimly burning.

No useless coffin enclosed his breast,
  Not in sheet or in shroud we wound him;
But he lay like a warrior taking his rest
  With his martial cloak around him.

Few and short were the prayers we said,
  And we spoke not a word of sorrow;
But we steadfastly gazed on the face that was dead,
  And we bitterly thought of the morrow.

We thought, as we hollow'd his narrow bed
  And smooth'd down his lonely pillow,
That the foe and the stranger would tread o'er his head,
  And we far away on the billow!

Lightly they'll talk of the spirit that's gone,
  And o'er his cold ashes upbraid him—
But little he'll reck, if they let him sleep on
  In the grave where a Briton has laid him.

But half of our heavy task was done
  When the clock struck the hour for retiring;
And we heard the distant and random gun
  That the foe was sullenly firing.

Slowly and sadly we laid him down,
  From the field of his fame fresh and gory;
We carved not a line, and we raised not a stone,
  But we left him alone with his glory.

CHARLES WOLFE (1791–1823)
[386]

Ode on the Death of the Duke of Wellington

WHO is he that cometh, like an honour'd guest,
With banner and with music, with soldier and with priest,
With a nation weeping, and breaking on my rest?
Mighty seaman, this is he
Was great by land as thou by sea.
Thine island loves thee well, thou famous man,
The greatest sailor since our world began.
Now, to the roll of muffled drums,
To thee the greatest soldier comes;
For this is he
Was great by land as thou by sea;
His foes were thine; he kept us free;
O give him welcome, this is he,
Worthy of our gorgeous rites,
And worthy to be laid by thee;
For this is England's greatest son,
He that gain'd a hundred fights,
Nor ever lost an English gun;
This is he that far away
Against the myriads of Assaye
Clash'd with his fiery few and won;
And underneath another sun,
Warring on a later day,
Round affrighted Lisbon drew
The treble works, the vast designs
Of his labour'd rampart-lines,
Where he greatly stood at bay,
Whence he issued forth anew,
And ever great and greater grew,
Beating from the wasted vines
Back to France her banded swarms,

Back to France with countless blows,
Till o'er the hills her eagles flew
Beyond the Pyrenean pines,
Follow'd up in valley and glen
With blare of bugle, clamour of men,
Roll of cannon and clash of arms,
And England pouring on her foes.
Such a war had such a close.
Again their ravening eagle rose
In anger, wheel'd on Europe-shadowing wings,
And barking for the thrones of kings;
Till one that sought but Duty's iron crown
On that loud sabbath shook the spoiler down;
A day of onsets of despair!
Dash'd on every rocky square
Their surging charges foam'd themselves away;
Last, the Prussian trumpet blew;
Thro' the long-tormented air
Heaven flash'd a sudden jubilant ray,
And down we swept and charged and overthrew.
So great a soldier taught us there,
What long-enduring hearts could do
In that world-earthquake, Waterloo!
Mighty seaman, tender and true,
And pure as he from taint of craven guile,
O saviour of the silver-coasted isle,
O shaker of the Baltic and the Nile,
If aught of things that here befall
Touch a spirit among things divine,
If love of country move thee there at all,
Be glad, because his bones are laid by thine!
And thro' the centuries let a people's voice
In full acclaim,

A people's voice,
The proof and echo of all human fame,
A people's voice, when they rejoice
At civic revel and pomp and game,
Attest their great commander's claim
With honour, honour, honour, honour to him,
Eternal honour to his name.

ALFRED, LORD TENNYSON (1809–92)

The Charge of the Light Brigade

I

HALF a league, half a league,
   Half a league onward,
All in the valley of Death
   Rode the six hundred.
'Forward, the Light Brigade!
Charge for the guns!' he said:
Into the valley of Death
   Rode the six hundred.

II

'Forward, the Light Brigade!'
Was there a man dismay'd?
Not tho' the soldier knew
   Some one had blunder'd:
Theirs not to make reply,
Theirs not to reason why,
Theirs but to do and die:
Into the valley of Death
   Rode the six hundred.

III

Cannon to right of them,
Cannon to left of them,
Cannon in front of them
 Volley'd and thunder'd;
Storm'd at with shot and shell,
Boldly they rode and well,
Into the jaws of Death,
Into the mouth of Hell
 Rode the six hundred.

IV

Flash'd all their sabres bare,
Flash'd as they turn'd in air,
Sabring the gunners there,
Charging an army, while
 All the world wonder'd:
Plunged in the battery-smoke
Right thro' the line they broke;
Cossack and Russian
Reel'd from the sabre-stroke
 Shatter'd and sunder'd.
Then they rode back, but not,
 Not the six hundred.

V

Cannon to right of them,
Cannon to left of them,
Cannon behind them
 Volley'd and thunder'd;
Storm'd at with shot and shell,
While horse and hero fell,
They that had fought so well

Came thro' the jaws of Death
Back from the mouth of Hell,
All that was left of them,
   Left of six hundred.

VI

When can their glory fade?
O the wild charge they made!
   All the world wonder'd.
Honour the charge they made!
Honour the Light Brigade,
   Noble six hundred!

ALFRED, LORD TENNYSON

' *Men who march away* ' (1914)

(Song of the Soldiers)

WHAT of the faith and fire within us
   Men who march away
   Ere the barn-cocks say
   Night is growing gray,
Leaving all that here can win us;
What of the faith and fire within us
   Men who march away?

Is it a purblind prank, O think you,
   Friend with the musing eye,
   Who watch us stepping by
   With doubt and dolorous sigh?
Can much pondering so hoodwink you?
Is it a purblind prank, O think you,
   Friend with the musing eye?

[391]

Nay. We well see what we are doing,
　　Though some may not see—
　　Dalliers as they be—
　　England's need are we;
Her distress would leave us ruing:
Nay. We well see what we are doing,
　　Though some may not see!

In our heart of hearts believing
　　Victory crowns the just,
　　And that braggarts must
　　Surely bite the dust,
' Press we to the field ungrieving ',
In our heart of hearts believing
　　Victory crowns the just.

Hence the faith and fire within us
　　Men who march away
　　Ere the barn-cocks say
　　Night is growing gray,
Leaving all that here can win us;
Hence the faith and fire within us
　　Men who march away.

Thomas Hardy (b. 1840)

Called up

Come, tumble up, Lord Nelson, the British Fleet 's a-
　　looming!
Come, show a leg, Lord Nelson, the guns they are a-
　　booming!
'Tis a longish line of battle—such as we did never see;
An' 'tis not the same old round-shot as was fired by you
　　an' me!

What see'st thou, Sir Francis ?—Strange things I see
     appearing!
What hearest thou, Sir Francis ?—Strange sounds I do be
     hearing!
They are fighting in the heavens; they're at war beneath
     the sea!
Ay, their ways are mighty different from the ways o' you
     an' me!

See'st thou nought else, Sir Francis ?—I see great lights
     a-seeking!
Hearest thou nought else, Sir Francis ?—I hear thin wires
     a-speaking!
Three leagues that shot hath carried!—God, that such
     could ever be!
There's no mortal doubt, Lord Nelson—they ha' done
     wi' you and me!

Look thou again, Sir Francis !—I see the flags a-flapping!
Hearken once more, Sir Francis !—I hear the sticks a-
     tapping!
'Tis a sight that calls me hither !—'Tis a sound that bids
     me ' come '!
'Tis the old Trafalgar signal !—'Tis the beating of my
     drum!

*Art thou ready, good Sir Francis ? See, they wait upon the
     Quay !*—
Praise be to God, Lord Nelson, they ha' thought of you an'
     me!

                    DUDLEY CLARK (b. 1899)

VII

Freedom

A! Fredome is a noble thing!
Fredome mayse man to haif liking;
Fredome all solace to man giffis,
He livis at ese that frely livis!
A noble hart may haif nane ese,
Na ellys nocht that may him plese,
Gif fredome fail'th; for fre liking
Is yharnit ouer all othir thing.
Na he that ay has livit fre
May nocht knaw well the propertè,
The anger, na the wretchit doom
That is couplit to foul thraldome.
But gif he had assayit it,
Then all perquer he suld it wit;
And suld think fredome mar to prise
Than all the gold in warld that is.

JOHN BARBOUR (1316?–95)

Yet, Freedom! yet thy Banner, torn but flying

Yet, Freedom! yet thy banner, torn but flying,
Streams like the thunder-storm *against* the wind;
Thy trumpet voice, though broken now and dying,
The loudest still the tempest leaves behind;
Thy tree hath lost its blossoms, and the rind,
Chopp'd by the axe, looks rough and little worth,
But the sap lasts,—and still the seed we find
Sown deep, even in the bosom of the North;
So shall a better spring less bitter fruit bring forth.

LORD BYRON (1788–1824)

mayse] makes.　　yharnit] yearned for.　　perquer] *par cœur,*
by experience.　　mar] more.

Battle Song

DAY, like our souls, is fiercely dark;
    What then? 'Tis day!
We sleep no more; the cock crows—hark!
    To arms! away!
They come! they come! the knell is rung
    Of us or them;
Wide o'er their march the pomp is flung
    Of gold and gem.
What collar'd hound of lawless sway,
    To famine dear—
What pension'd slave of Attila,
    Leads in the rear?
Come they from Scythian wilds afar,
    Our blood to spill?
Wear they the livery of the Czar?
    They do his will.
Nor tassell'd silk, nor epaulet,
    Nor plume, nor torse—
No splendour gilds, all sternly met,
    Our foot and horse.
But, dark and still, we inly glow,
    Condensed in ire!
Strike, tawdry slaves, and ye shall know
    Our gloom is fire.
In vain your pomp, ye evil powers,
    Insults the land;
Wrongs, vengeance, and the Cause are ours,
    And God's right hand!
Madmen! they trample into snakes
    The wormy clod!
Like fire, beneath their feet awakes
    The sword of God!

[395]

Behind, before, above, below,
    They rouse the brave;
Where'er they go, they make a foe,
    Or find a grave.

EBENEZER ELLIOTT (1781–1849)

How Sleep the Brave

How sleep the brave, who sink to rest
By all their country's wishes blest!
When Spring, with dewy fingers cold,
Returns to deck their hallow'd mould,
She there shall dress a sweeter sod
Than Fancy's feet have ever trod.

By fairy hands their knell is rung;
By forms unseen their dirge is sung;
There Honour comes, a pilgrim grey,
To bless the turf that wraps their clay;
And Freedom shall awhile repair
To dwell, a weeping hermit, there!

WILLIAM COLLINS (1721–59)

Patriotism

BREATHES there the man with soul so dead,
Who never to himself hath said,
  'This is my own, my native land!'
Whose heart hath ne'er within him burn'd
As home his footsteps he hath turn'd
  From wandering on a foreign strand?

SIR WALTER SCOTT (1771–1832)

Sound, sound the Clarion

SOUND, sound the clarion, fill the fife!
　　To all the sensual world proclaim,
One crowded hour of glorious life
　　Is worth an age without a name.

SIR WALTER SCOTT (?)

The Isles of Greece

THE isles of Greece! the isles of Greece!
　　Where burning Sappho loved and sung,
Where grew the arts of war and peace,
　　Where Delos rose, and Phoebus sprung!
Eternal summer gilds them yet,
But all, except their sun, is set.

The Scian and the Teian muse,
　　The hero's harp, the lover's lute,
Have found the fame your shores refuse:
　　Their place of birth alone is mute
To sounds which echo further west
Than your sires' ' Islands of the Blest '.

The mountains look on Marathon—
　　And Marathon looks on the sea;
And musing there an hour alone,
　　I dream'd that Greece might still be free;
For standing on the Persians' grave,
I could not deem myself a slave.

A king sate on the rocky brow
　　Which looks o'er sea-born Salamis;
And ships, by thousands, lay below,
　　And men in nations;—all were his!
He counted them at break of day—
And when the sun set, where were they?

[397]

And where are they? and where art thou,
   My country? On thy voiceless shore
The heroic lay is tuneless now—
   The heroic bosom beats no more!
And must thy lyre, so long divine,
Degenerate into hands like mine?

'Tis something in the dearth of fame,
   Though link'd among a fetter'd race,
To feel at least a patriot's shame,
   Even as I sing, suffuse my face;
For what is left the poet here?
For Greeks a blush—for Greece a tear.

Must *we* but weep o'er days more blest?
   Must *we* but blush?—Our fathers bled.
Earth! render back from out thy breast
   A remnant of our Spartan dead!
Of the three hundred grant but three,
To make a new Thermopylae!

What, silent still? and silent all?
   Ah! no;—the voices of the dead
Sound like a distant torrent's fall,
   And answer, 'Let one living head,
But one, arise,—we come, we come!'
'Tis but the living who are dumb.

In vain—in vain: strike other chords;
   Fill high the cup with Samian wine!
Leave battles to the Turkish hordes,
   And shed the blood of Scio's vine!
Hark! rising to the ignoble call—
How answers each bold Bacchanal!

You have the Pyrrhic dance as yet;
   Where is the Pyrrhic phalanx gone?
Of two such lessons, why forget
   The nobler and the manlier one?
You have the letters Cadmus gave—
Think ye he meant them for a slave?

Fill high the bowl with Samian wine!
   We will not think of themes like these!
It made Anacreon's song divine:
   He served—but served Polycrates—
A tyrant; but our masters then
Were still, at least, our countrymen.

The tyrant of the Chersonese
   Was freedom's best and bravest friend;
That tyrant was Miltiades!
   O that the present hour would lend
Another despot of the kind!
Such chains as his were sure to bind.

Fill high the bowl with Samian wine!
   On Suli's rock, and Parga's shore,
Exists the remnant of a line
   Such as the Doric mothers bore;
And there, perhaps, some seed is sown,
The Heracleidan blood might own.

Trust not for freedom to the Franks—
   They have a king who buys and sells;
In native swords and native ranks
   The only hope of courage dwells:
But Turkish force and Latin fraud
Would break your shield, however broad.

Fill high the bowl with Samian wine!
 Our virgins dance beneath the shade—
I see their glorious black eyes shine;
 But gazing on each glowing maid,
My own the burning tear-drop laves,
To think such breasts must suckle slaves.

Place me on Sunium's marbled steep,
 Where nothing, save the waves and I,
May hear our mutual murmurs sweep;
 There, swan-like, let me sing and die:
A land of slaves shall ne'er be mine—
Dash down yon cup of Samian wine!

     LORD BYRON (1788–1824)

Hellas

THE world's great age begins anew,
 The golden years return,
The earth doth like a snake renew
 Her winter weeds outworn:
Heaven smiles, and faiths and empires gleam
Like wrecks of a dissolving dream.

A brighter Hellas rears its mountains
 From waves serener far;
A new Peneus rolls his fountains
 Against the morning star;
Where fairer Tempe bloom, there sleep
Young Cyclads on a sunnier deep.

A loftier Argo cleaves the main,
 Fraught with a later prize;
Another Orpheus sings again,
 And loves, and weeps, and dies;
A new Ulysses leaves once more
Calypso for his native shore.

[400]

O write no more the tale of Troy,
   If earth Death's scroll must be—
Nor mix with Laian rage the joy
   Which dawns upon the free,
Although a subtler Sphinx renew
Riddles of death Thebes never knew.

Another Athens shall arise,
   And to remoter time
Bequeath, like sunset to the skies,
   The splendour of its prime;
And leave, if naught so bright may live,
All earth can take or Heaven can give.

Saturn and Love their long repose
   Shall burst, more bright and good
Than all who fell, than One who rose,
   Than many unsubdued:
Not gold, not blood, their altar dowers,
But votive tears and symbol flowers.

O cease! must hate and death return?
   Cease! must men kill and die?
Cease! drain not to its dregs the urn
   Of bitter prophecy!
The world is weary of the past—
O might it die or rest at last!

PERCY BYSSHE SHELLEY

(1792–1822)

Men of England

MEN of England! who inherit
    Rights that cost your sires their blood!
Men whose undegenerate spirit
    Has been proved on land and flood

By the foes ye've fought, uncounted,
    By the glorious deeds ye've done,
Trophies captured—breaches mounted,
    Navies conquered—kingdoms won!

Yet, remember, England gathers
    Hence but fruitless wreaths of fame,
If the freedom of your fathers
    Glow not in your hearts the same.

What are monuments of bravery,
    Where no public virtues bloom?
What avail in lands of slavery
    Trophied temples, arch, and tomb?

Pageants!—Let the world revere us
    For our people's rights and laws,
And the breasts of civic heroes
    Bared in Freedom's holy cause.

Yours are Hampden's, Russell's glory,
    Sydney's matchless shade is yours,—
Martyrs in heroic story
    Worth a hundred Agincourts!

We're the sons of sires that baffled
    Crowned and mitred tyranny:—
They defied the field and scaffold
    For their birthrights—so will we!

THOMAS CAMPBELL

(1777–1844)

Home-Thoughts, from the Sea

NOBLY, nobly Cape Saint Vincent to the North-west died
    away;
Sunset ran, one glorious blood-red, reeking into Cadiz
    Bay;
Bluish 'mid the burning water, full in face Trafalgar lay;

In the dimmest North-east distance dawn'd Gibraltar
    grand and gray;
' Here and here did England help me: how can I help
    England? '—say,
Whoso turns as I, this evening, turn to God to praise and
    pray,
While Jove's planet rises yonder, silent over Africa.

ROBERT BROWNING

(1812–89)

England, my England

WHAT have I done for you,
   England, my England?
What is there I would not do,
   England, my own?
With your glorious eyes austere,
As the Lord were walking near,
Whispering terrible things and dear
   As the Song on your bugles blown,
     England—
   Round the world on your bugles blown!

Where shall the watchful sun,
   England, my England,
Match the master-work you've done,
   England, my own?
When shall he rejoice agen
Such a breed of mighty men
As come forward, one to ten,
   To the Song on your bugles blown,
     England—
   Down the years on your bugles blown?

Ever the faith endures,
   England, my England:—
'Take and break us: we are yours,
   England, my own!
Life is good, and joy runs high
Between English earth and sky:

Death is death; but we shall die
    To the Song on your bugles blown,
        England—
    To the stars on your bugles blown!'

They call you proud and hard,
    England, my England:
You with worlds to watch and ward,
    England, my own!
You whose mail'd hand keeps the keys
Of such teeming destinies,
You could know nor dread nor ease
    Were the Song on your bugles blown,
        England,
    Round the Pit on your bugles blown!

Mother of Ships whose might,
    England, my England,
Is the fierce old Sea's delight,
    England, my own,
Chosen daughter of the Lord,
Spouse-in-Chief of the ancient Sword,
There's the menace of the Word
    In the Song on your bugles blown,
        England—
    Out of heaven on your bugles blown!

WILLIAM ERNEST HENLEY

(1849–1903)

Adlestrop

YES. I remember Adlestrop—
The name, because one afternoon
Of heat the express-train drew up there
Unwontedly.   It was late June.

The steam hissed.   Some one cleared his throat.
No one left and no one came
On the bare platform.   What I saw
Was Adlestrop—only a name

And willows, willow-herb, and grass,
And meadowsweet, and haycocks dry,
No whit less still and lonely fair
Than the high cloudlets in the sky.

And for that minute a blackbird sang
Close by, and round him, mistier,
Farther and farther, all the birds
Of Oxfordshire and Gloucestershire.

EDWARD THOMAS
(1877–1917)

The South Country

WHEN I am living in the Midlands
    That are sodden and unkind,
I light my lamp in the evening:
    My work is left behind;
And the great hills of the South Country
    Come back into my mind.

The great hills of the South Country
   They stand along the sea;
And it's there walking in the high woods
   That I could wish to be,
And the men that were boys when I was a boy
   Walking along with me.

The men that live in North England
   I saw them for a day:
Their hearts are set upon the waste fells,
   Their skies are fast and grey;
From their castle-walls a man may see
   The mountains far away.

The men that live in West England
   They see the Severn strong,
A-rolling on rough water brown
   Light aspen leaves along.
They have the secret of the Rocks,
   And the oldest kind of song.

But the men that live in the South Country
   Are the kindest and most wise,
They get their laughter from the loud surf,
   And the faith in their happy eyes
Comes surely from our Sister the Spring
   When over the sea she flies;
The violets suddenly bloom at her feet,
   She blesses us with surprise.

I never get between the pines
   But I smell the Sussex air;
Nor I never come on a belt of sand
   But my home is there.
And along the sky the line of the Downs
   So noble and so bare.

[407]

A lost thing could I never find,
  Nor a broken thing mend:
And I fear I shall be all alone
  When I get towards the end.
Who will there be to comfort me
  Or who will be my friend?

I will gather and carefully make my friends
  Of the men of the Sussex Weald,
They watch the stars from silent folds,
  They stiffly plough the field.
By them and the God of the South Country
  My poor soul shall be healed.

If I ever become a rich man,
  Or if ever I grow to be old,
I will build a house with deep thatch
  To shelter me from the cold,
And there shall the Sussex songs be sung
  And the story of Sussex told.

I will hold my house in the high wood
  Within a walk of the sea,
And the men that were boys when I was a boy
  Shall sit and drink with me.

                    HILAIRE BELLOC
                       (b. 1870)

Sussex

God gave all men all earth to love,
    But since our hearts are small,
Ordained for each one spot should prove
    Belovèd over all;
That, as He watched Creation's birth,
    So we, in godlike mood,
May of our love create our earth
    And see that it is good.

So one shall Baltic pines content,
    As one some Surrey glade,
Or one the palm-grove's droned lament
    Before Levuka's Trade.
Each to his choice, and I rejoice
    The lot has fallen to me
In a fair ground—in a fair ground—
    Yea, Sussex by the sea!

No tender-hearted garden crowns,
    No bosomed woods adorn
Our blunt, bow-headed, whale-backed Downs,
    But gnarled and writhen thorn—
Bare slopes where chasing shadows skim,
    And, through the gaps revealed,
Belt upon belt, the wooded, dim
    Blue goodness of the Weald.

Clean of officious fence or hedge,
    Half-wild and wholly tame,
The wise turf cloaks the white cliff edge
    As when the Romans came.

Levuka] one of the Fiji Islands.   Trade] Trade-wind.

What sign of those that fought and died
  At shift of sword and sword?
The barrow and the camp abide,
  The sunlight and the sward.

Here leaps ashore the full Sou'west
  All heavy-winged with brine,
Here lies above the folded crest
  The Channel's leaden line;
And here the sea-fogs lap and cling,
  And here, each warning each,
The sheep-bells and the ship-bells ring
  Along the hidden beach.

We have no waters to delight
  Our broad and brookless vales—
Only the dewpond on the height,
  Unfed, that never fails—
Whereby no tattered herbage tells
  Which way the season flies—
Only our close-bit thyme that smells
  Like dawn in Paradise.

Here through the strong and shadeless days
  The tinkling silence thrills;
Or little, lost, Down churches praise
  The Lord who made the hills:
But here the Old Gods guard their round,
  And, in her secret heart,
The heathen kingdom Wilfrid found
  Dreams, as she dwells, apart.

Though all the rest were all my share,
    With equal soul I'd see
Her nine-and-thirty sisters fair,
    Yet none more fair than she.
Choose ye your need from Thames to Tweed,
    And I will choose instead
Such lands as lie 'twixt Rake and Rye,
    Black Down and Beachy Head.

I will go out against the sun
    Where the rolled scarp retires,
And the Long Man of Wilmington
    Looks naked toward the shires;
And east till doubling Rother crawls
    To find the fickle tide,
By dry and sea-forgotten walls,
    Our ports of stranded pride.

I will go north about the shaws
    And the deep ghylls that breed
Huge oaks and old, the which we hold
    No more than Sussex weed;
Or south where windy Piddinghoe's
    Begilded dolphin veers,
And black beside wide-bankèd Ouse
    Lie down our Sussex steers.

So to the land our hearts we give
    Till the sure magic strike,
And Memory, Use, and Love make live
    Us and our fields alike—

        shaws] woods.   ghylls] glens.

That deeper than our speech and thought,
    Beyond our reason's sway,
Clay of the pit whence we were wrought
    Yearns to its fellow-clay.

God gives all men all earth to love,
    But since man's heart is small,
Ordains for each one spot shall prove
    Belovèd over all.
Each to his choice, and I rejoice
    The lot has fallen to me
In a fair ground—in a fair ground—
    Yea, Sussex by the sea !

                            RUDYARD KIPLING
                                    (b. 1865)

At the Wars

Now that I am ta'en away,
And may not see another day,
What is it to my eye appears?
What sound rings in my stricken ears?
Not even the voice of any friend
Or eyes beloved-world-without-end,
But scenes and sounds of the countryside
In far England across the tide:
An upland field when Spring's begun,
Mellow beneath the evening sun. . . .
A circle of loose and lichened wall
Over which seven red pines fall. . . .
An orchard of wizen blossoming trees
Wherein the nesting chaffinches

Begin again the self-same song
All the late April day-time long. . . .
Paths that lead a shelving course
Between the chalk scarp and the gorse
By English downs; and, O! too well
I hear the hidden, clanking bell
Of wandering sheep . . . I see the brown
Twilight of the huge empty down. . . .
Soon blotted out! for now a lane
Glitters with warmth of May-time rain,
And on a shooting briar I see
A yellow bird who sings to me.

O yellow-hammer, once I heard
Thy yaffle when no other bird
Could to my sunk heart comfort bring;
But now I would not have thee sing,
So sharp thy note is with the pain
Of England I may not see again!
Yet sing thy song: there answereth
Deep in me a voice which saith:
' *The gorse upon the twilit down,*
The English loam so sunset brown,
The bowed pines and the sheep-bells' clamour,
The wet, lit lane and the yellow-hammer,
The orchard and the chaffinch song,
Only to the Brave belong.
And he shall lose their joy for aye
If their price he cannot pay,
Who shall find them dearer far
Enriched by blood after long War.'

ROBERT NICHOLS (b. 1893)

yaffle] Here used of the yellow-hammer's note.

[413]

The Soldier

IF I should die, think only this of me:
  That there's some corner of a foreign field
That is for ever England. There shall be
  In that rich earth a richer dust concealed;
A dust whom England bore, shaped, made aware,
  Gave, once, her flowers to love, her ways to roam,
A body of England's breathing English air,
  Washed by the rivers, blest by suns of home.

And think, this heart, all evil shed away,
  A pulse in the eternal mind, no less
    Gives somewhere back the thoughts by England
        given;
Her sights and sounds; dreams happy as her day;
  And laughter, learnt of friends; and gentleness,
    In hearts at peace, under an English heaven.

RUPERT BROOKE (1887–1915)

Epitaph on an Army of Mercenaries

THESE, in the day when heaven was falling,
  The hour when earth's foundations fled,
Followed their mercenary calling
  And took their wages and are dead.

Their shoulders held the sky suspended;
  They stood, and earth's foundations stay;
What God abandoned, these defended,
  And saved the sum of things for pay.

A. E. HOUSMAN (b. 1859)

For the Fallen

WITH proud thanksgiving, a mother for her children,
England mourns for her dead across the sea.
Flesh of her flesh they were, spirit of her spirit,
Fallen in the cause of the free.

Solemn the drums thrill: Death august and royal
Sings sorrow up into immortal spheres.
There is music in the midst of desolation
And a glory that shines upon our tears.

They went with songs to the battle, they were young,
Straight of limb, true of eye, steady and aglow.
They were staunch to the end against odds uncounted,
They fell with their faces to the foe.

They shall grow not old, as we that are left grow old:
Age shall not weary them, nor the years condemn.
At the going down of the sun and in the morning
We will remember them.

They mingle not with their laughing comrades again;
They sit no more at familiar tables of home;
They have no lot in our labour of the day-time;
They sleep beyond England's foam.

But where our desires are and our hopes profound,
Felt as a well-spring that is hidden from sight,
To the innermost heart of their own land they are known
As the stars are known to the Night.

As the stars that shall be bright when we are dust,
Moving in marches upon the heavenly plain,
As the stars that are starry in the time of our darkness,
To the end, to the end, they remain.

LAURENCE BINYON (b. 1869)

[415]

VIII

Annan Water

' ANNAN Water's wading deep,
  And my Love Annie's wondrous bonny;
And I am loath she shall wet her feet,
  Because I love her best of ony.'

He's loupen on his bonny gray,
  He rode the right gate and the ready;
For all the storm he wadna stay,
  For seeking of his bonny lady.

And he has ridden o'er field and fell,
  Through moor, and moss, and many a mire;
His spurs of steel were sair to bide,
  And from her four feet flew the fire.

' My bonny gray, now play your part!
  If ye be the steed that wins my dearie,
With corn and hay ye'll feed for aye,
  And never spur shall make you wearie!'

The gray was a mare, and a right gude mare;
  But when she wan the Annan Water,
She could not have ridden the ford that night
  Had a thousand merks been wadded at her.

' O boatman, boatman, put off your boat,
  Put off your boat for golden money!'
But for all the gold in fair Scotland,
  He dared not take him through to Annie.

wadded] wagered.
[416]

' O I was sworn so late yestreen,
   Not by a single oath, but mony!
I'll cross the drumly stream to-night,
   Or never could I face my honey!'

The side was stey, and the bottom deep,
   From bank to brae the water pouring;
The bonny gray mare she swat for fear,
   For she heard the water kelpy roaring.

He spurr'd her forth into the flood,
   I wot she swam both strong and steady;
But the stream was broad, and her strength did fail,
   And he never saw his bonny lady!

ANONYMOUS (16th century?)

The Lowlands of Holland

' MY love he's built a bonnie ship, and set her on the sea,
With seven score guid mariners to bear her companie.
There's three score is sunk, and three score dead at sea;
And the Lowlands of Holland hae twined my love and me.

' My love he built another ship, and set her on the main,
And nane but twenty mariners for to bring her hame;
But the weary wind began to rise, and the sea began to
    rout;
My love then, and his bonnie ship, turned withershins
    about.

' There shall neither coif come on my head, nor kame come
    in my hair;
There shall neither coal nor candle-licht come in my bouir
    mair;

drumly] turbid.   stey] steep.   withershins] from right to left.

Nor will I love another man until the day I dee,
For I never loved a love but ane, and he's drown'd in the
   sea.'

'O haud your tongue, my daughter dear, be still and be
   content;
There are mair lads in Galloway, ye need na sair lament.'
'O! there is nane in Galloway, there's nane at a' for me;
For I never loved a love but ane, and he's drown'd in
   the sea.'
       ANONYMOUS (16th century?)

The Lament of the Border Widow

MY love he built me a bonny bower,
And clad it a' wi' lilye flow'r,
A brawer bower ye ne'er did see,
Than my true love he built for me.

There came a man, by middle day,
He spied his sport, and went away;
And brought the king that very night,
Who brake my bower, and slew my knight.

He slew my knight, to me sae dear;
He slew my knight, and poin'd his gear;
My servants all for life did flee,
And left me in extremitie.

I sew'd his sheet, making my mane;
I watched the corpse, myself alane;
I watched his body, night and day;
No living creature came that way.

I took his body on my back,
And whiles I gaed, and whiles I sat;
I digg'd a grave, and laid him in,
And happ'd him with the sod sae green.

  poin'd] confiscated.   happ'd] covered.

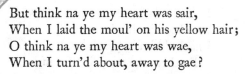

But think na ye my heart was sair,
When I laid the moul' on his yellow hair;
O think na ye my heart was wae,
When I turn'd about, away to gae?

Nae living man I'll love again,
Since that my lovely knight is slain;
Wi' ae lock of his yellow hair
I'll chain my heart for evermair.

ANONYMOUS (16th century?)

Helen of Kirconnell

I WISH I were where Helen lies,
Night and day on me she cries;
O that I were where Helen lies,
  On fair Kirconnell lea!

Curst be the heart that thought the thought,
And curst the hand that fired the shot,
When in my arms burd Helen dropt,
  And died to succour me!

O think na ye my heart was sair,
When my Love dropp'd and spak nae mair!
There did she swoon wi' meikle care,
  On fair Kirconnell lea.

As I went down the water-side,
None but my foe to be my guide,
None but my foe to be my guide,
  On fair Kirconnell lea;

[419]

I lighted down my sword to draw,
I hackèd him in pieces sma',
I hackèd him in pieces sma',
   For her sake that died for me.

O Helen fair, beyond compare!
I'll mak a garland o' thy hair,
Shall bind my heart for evermair,
   Until the day I die!

O that I were where Helen lies!
Night and day on me she cries;
Out of my bed she bids me rise,
   Says, ' Haste, and come to me!'

O Helen fair! O Helen chaste!
If I were with thee, I'd be blest,
Where thou lies low and taks thy rest,
   On fair Kirconnell lea.

I wish my grave were growing green,
A winding-sheet drawn owre my e'en,
And I in Helen's arms lying,
   On fair Kirconnell lea.

I wish I were where Helen lies!
Night and day on me she cries;
And I am weary of the skies,
   For her sake that died for me.

ANONYMOUS (17th century)

The Bonny Earl of Murray

YE Highlands and ye Lawlands,
  O where hae ye been?
They hae slain the Earl of Murray,
  And hae laid him on the green.

[420]

Now wae be to thee, Huntley!
    And whairfore did ye sae!
I bade you bring him wi' you,
    But forbade you him to slay.

He was a braw gallant,
    And he rid at the ring;
And the bonny Earl of Murray,
    O he might hae been a king!

He was a braw gallant,
    And he play'd at the ba';
And the bonny Earl of Murray
    Was the flower amang them a'!

He was a braw gallant,
    And he play'd at the gluve;
And the bonny Earl of Murray,
    O he was the Queen's luve!

O lang will his Lady
    Look owre the Castle Downe,
Ere she see the Earl of Murray
    Come sounding through the town!

                    ANONYMOUS (16th century)

Fidele

FEAR no more the heat o' the sun,
    Nor the furious winter's rages;
Thou thy worldly task hast done,
    Home art gone, and ta'en thy wages:
Golden lads and girls all must,
As chimney-sweepers, come to dust.

[421]

Fear no more the frown o' the great,
   Thou art past the tyrant's stroke;
Care no more to clothe and eat;
   To thee the reed is as the oak:
The sceptre, learning, physic, must
All follow this, and come to dust.

Fear no more the lightning-flash,
   Nor the all-dreaded thunder-stone;
Fear not slander, censure rash;
   Thou hast finish'd joy and moan:
All lovers young, all lovers must
Consign to thee, and come to dust.

No exorciser harm thee!
Nor no witchcraft charm thee!
Ghost unlaid forbear thee!
Nothing ill come near thee!
Quiet consummation have;
And renownèd be thy grave!

          WILLIAM SHAKESPEARE (1564–1616)

On the Tombs in Westminster Abbey

MORTALITY, behold and fear!
What a change of flesh is here!
Think how many royal bones
Sleep within this heap of stones:
Here they lie had realms and lands,
Who now want strength to stir their hands:
Where from their pulpits seal'd with dust
They preach, ' In greatness is no trust.'
Here 's an acre sown indeed
With the richest, royall'st seed

[422]

That the earth did e'er suck in
Since the first man died for sin:
Here the bones of birth have cried—
'Though gods they were, as men they died.'
Here are sands, ignoble things,
Dropt from the ruin'd sides of kings;
Here's a world of pomp and state,
Buried in dust, once dead by fate.

FRANCIS BEAUMONT (1584–1616)

Death the Leveller

THE glories of our blood and state
    Are shadows, not substantial things;
There is no armour against Fate;
    Death lays his icy hand on kings:
            Sceptre and Crown
            Must tumble down,
And in the dust be equal made,
With the poor crookèd scythe and spade.

Some men with swords may reap the field,
    And plant fresh laurels where they kill:
But their strong nerves at last must yield;
    They tame but one another still:
            Early or late
            They stoop to fate,
And must give up their murmuring breath
When they, pale captives, creep to death.

The garlands wither on your brow;
    Then boast no more your mighty deeds!
Upon Death's purple altar now
    See where the victor-victim bleeds.

[423]

Your heads must come
To the cold tomb:
Only the actions of the just
Smell sweet and blossom in their dust.

JAMES SHIRLEY (1596–1666)

Elegy Written in a Country Churchyard

THE curfew tolls the knell of parting day,
  The lowing herd wind slowly o'er the lea,
The plowman homeward plods his weary way,
  And leaves the world to darkness and to me.

Now fades the glimmering landscape on the sight,
  And all the air a solemn stillness holds,
Save where the beetle wheels his droning flight,
  And drowsy tinklings lull the distant folds:

Save that from yonder ivy-mantled tow'r
  The moping owl does to the moon complain
Of such as, wand'ring near her secret bow'r,
  Molest her ancient solitary reign.

Beneath those rugged elms, that yew-tree's shade,
  Where heaves the turf in many a mould'ring heap,
Each in his narrow cell for ever laid,
  The rude forefathers of the hamlet sleep.

The breezy call of incense-breathing morn,
  The swallow twitt'ring from the straw-built shed,
The cock's shrill clarion, or the echoing horn,
  No more shall rouse them from their lowly bed.

For them no more the blazing hearth shall burn,
  Or busy housewife ply her evening care:
No children run to lisp their sire's return,
  Or climb his knees the envied kiss to share.

Oft did the harvest to their sickle yield,
    Their furrow oft the stubborn glebe has broke:
How jocund did they drive their team afield!
    How bow'd the woods beneath their sturdy stroke!

Let not Ambition mock their useful toil,
    Their homely joys, and destiny obscure;
Nor Grandeur hear with a disdainful smile
    The short and simple annals of the poor.

The boast of heraldry, the pomp of pow'r,
    And all that beauty, all that wealth e'er gave,
Awaits alike th' inevitable hour:
    The paths of glory lead but to the grave.

Nor you, ye proud, impute to these the fault
    If Memory o'er their tomb no trophies raise,
Where through the long-drawn aisle and fretted vault
    The pealing anthem swells the note of praise.

Can storied urn or animated bust
    Back to its mansion call the fleeting breath?
Can Honour's voice provoke the silent dust,
    Or Flatt'ry soothe the dull cold ear of death?

Perhaps in this neglected spot is laid
    Some heart once pregnant with celestial fire;
Hands, that the rod of empire might have sway'd,
    Or waked to ecstasy the living lyre.

But Knowledge to their eyes her ample page
    Rich with the spoils of time did ne'er unroll;
Chill Penury repress'd their noble rage,
    And froze the genial current of the soul.

Full many a gem of purest ray serene
    The dark unfathom'd caves of ocean bear:
Full many a flower is born to blush unseen,
    And waste its sweetness on the desert air.

Some village Hampden that with dauntless breast
    The little tyrant of his fields withstood,
Some mute inglorious Milton here may rest,
    Some Cromwell guiltless of his country's blood.

Th' applause of list'ning senates to command,
    The threats of pain and ruin to despise,
To scatter plenty o'er a smiling land,
    And read their history in a nation's eyes—

Their lot forbade: nor circumscribed alone
    Their growing virtues, but their crimes confined;
Forbade to wade thro' slaughter to a throne,
    And shut the gates of mercy on mankind;

The struggling pangs of conscious truth to hide,
    To quench the blushes of ingenuous shame,
Or heap the shrine of Luxury and Pride
    With incense kindled at the Muse's flame.

Far from the madding crowd's ignoble strife,
    Their sober wishes never learn'd to stray;
Along the cool, sequester'd vale of life
    They kept the noiseless tenor of their way.

Yet ev'n these bones from insult to protect
    Some frail memorial still erected nigh,
With uncouth rhymes and shapeless sculpture deck'd,
    Implores the passing tribute of a sigh.

[426]

Their name, their years, spelt by th' unletter'd Muse,
    The place of fame and elegy supply:
And many a holy text around she strews,
    That teach the rustic moralist to die.

For who, to dumb Forgetfulness a prey,
    This pleasing anxious being e'er resign'd,
Left the warm precincts of the cheerful day,
    Nor cast one longing ling'ring look behind?

On some fond breast the parting soul relies,
    Some pious drops the closing eye requires;
E'en from the tomb the voice of Nature cries,
    E'en in our ashes live their wonted fires.

For thee, who, mindful of th' unhonour'd dead,
    Dost in these lines their artless tale relate;
If chance, by lonely contemplation led,
    Some kindred spirit shall inquire thy fate—

Haply some hoary-headed swain may say,
    ' Oft have we seen him at the peep of dawn
Brushing with hasty steps the dews away
    To meet the sun upon the upland lawn.

' There at the foot of yonder nodding beech
    That wreathes its old fantastic roots so high,
His listless length at noontide would he stretch,
    And pore upon the brook that babbles by.

' Hard by yon wood, now smiling as in scorn,
    Mutt'ring his wayward fancies he would rove,
Now drooping, woeful-wan, like one forlorn,
    Or crazed with care, or cross'd in hopeless love.

'One morn I miss'd him on the custom'd hill,
  Along the heath, and near his favourite tree;
Another came; nor yet beside the rill,
  Nor up the lawn, nor at the wood was he;

'The next with dirges due in sad array
  Slow through the church-way path we saw him borne.
Approach and read (for thou canst read) the lay
  Graved on the stone beneath yon agèd thorn: '

THE EPITAPH

Here rests his head upon the lap of Earth
  A Youth, to Fortune and to Fame unknown.
Fair Science frown'd not on his humble birth,
  And Melancholy mark'd him for her own.

Large was his bounty, and his soul sincere,
  Heav'n did a recompense as largely send:
He gave to Mis'ry all he had, a tear,
  He gain'd from Heav'n ('twas all he wish'd) a friend.

No farther seek his merits to disclose
  Or draw his frailties from their dread abode,
(There they alike in trembling hope repose,)
  The bosom of his Father and his God.

THOMAS GRAY (1716–71)

The Flowers of the Forest

I'VE seen the smiling
Of Fortune beguiling;
I've felt all its favours, and found its decay:
Sweet was its blessing,
Kind its caressing;
But now it is fled—it is fled far away.

I've seen the forest
Adornèd the foremost
With flowers of the fairest most pleasant and gay:
Sae bonny was their blooming!
Their scent the air perfuming!
But now they are withered and weeded away.

I've seen the morning
With gold the hills adorning,
And loud tempest storming before the mid-day;
I've seen Tweed's silver streams,
Shining in the sunny beams,
Grow drumly and dark as he rowed on his way.

O fickle Fortune,
Why this cruel sporting?
Oh, why still perplex us, poor sons of a day?
Nae mair your smiles can cheer me,
Nae mair your frowns can fear me,
For the Flowers of the Forest are a' wede away.

ALISON COCKBURN (1712?–94)

A Lament for Flodden

I've heard them lilting at our ewe-milking,
Lasses a' lilting before dawn o' day;
But now they are moaning on ilka green loaning—
The Flowers of the Forest are a' wede away.

At bughts, in the morning, nae blythe lads are scorning,
Lasses are lonely and dowie and wae;
Nae daffing, nae gabbing, but sighing and sabbing,
Ilk ane lifts her leglin and hies her away.

bughts] folds.   daffing] jesting.   leglin] milking-pail.

In har'st, at the shearing, nae youths now are jeering,
    Bandsters are lyart, and runkled, and gray:
At fair or at preaching, nae wooing, nae fleeching—
    The Flowers of the Forest are a' wede away.

At e'en, in the gloaming, nae swankies are roaming
    'Bout stacks wi' the lasses at bogle to play;
But ilk ane sits eerie, lamenting her dearie—
    The Flowers of the Forest are a' wede away。

Dool and wae for the order sent our lads to the Border!
    The English, for ance, by guile wan the day;
The Flowers of the Forest, that fought ay the foremost,
    The prime of our land, lie cauld in the clay.

We'll hear nae mair lilting at our ewe-milking;
    Women and bairns are heartless and wae;
Sighing and moaning on ilka green loaning—
    The Flowers of the Forest are a' wede away.

                        JANE ELLIOT (1727–1805)

Auld Robin Gray

WHEN the sheep are in the fauld, and the kye at hame,
And a' the warld to rest are gane,
The waes o' my heart fa' in showers frae my e'e,
While my gudeman lies sound by me.

Young Jamie lo'ed me weel, and sought me for his bride;
But saving a croun he had naething else beside:
To make the croun a pund, young Jamie gaed to sea;
And the croun and the pund were baith for me.

lyart] hoary.   fleeching] entreaty.   swankies] swains.
bogle] barley-break.

He hadna been awa' a week but only twa,
When my father brak his arm, and the cow was stown
    awa';
My mother she fell sick, and my Jamie at the sea—
And auld Robin Gray came a-courtin' me.

My father couldna work, and my mother couldna spin;
I toil'd day and night, but their bread I couldna win;
Auld Rob maintain'd them baith, and wi' tears in his e'e
Said, Jennie, for their sakes, O, marry me!

My heart it said nay; I look'd for Jamie back;
But the wind it blew high, and the ship it was a wrack;
His ship it was a wrack—why didna Jamie dee?
Or why do I live to cry, Wae 's me?

My father urgit sair: my mother didna speak;
But she look'd in my face till my heart was like to break:
They gi'ed him my hand, but my heart was at the sea,
Sae auld Robin Gray he was gudeman to me.

I hadna been a wife a week but only four,
When mournfu' as I sat on the stane at the door,
I saw my Jamie's wraith, for I couldna think it he—
Till he said, I'm come hame to marry thee.

O sair, sair did we greet, and muckle did we say;
We took but ae kiss, and I bade him gang away:
I wish that I were dead, but I'm no like to dee;
And why was I born to say, Wae 's me!

I gang like a ghaist, and I carena to spin;
I daurna think on Jamie, for that wad be a sin;
But I'll do my best a gude wife ay to be,
For auld Robin Gray he is kind unto me.

LADY ANNE LINDSAY (1750–1825)

[431]

Proud Maisie

PROUD Maisie is in the wood,
    Walking so early;
Sweet Robin sits on the bush,
    Singing so rarely.

'Tell me, thou bonny bird,
    When shall I marry me?'
—'When six braw gentlemen
    Kirkward shall carry ye.'

'Who makes the bridal bed,
    Birdie, say truly?'
—'The grey-headed sexton
    That delves the grave duly.

'The glow-worm o'er grave and stone
    Shall light thee steady;
The owl from the steeple sing
    Welcome, proud lady!'

SIR WALTER SCOTT (1771–1832)

The Land o' the Leal

I'M wearin' awa', John,
Like snaw-wreaths in thaw, John,
I'm wearin' awa'
    To the land o' the leal.
There's nae sorrow there, John,
There's neither cauld nor care, John,
The day is ay fair
    In the land o' the leal.

[432]

Our bonnie bairn's there, John,
She was baith gude and fair, John;
And O! we grudged her sair
    To the land o' the leal.
But sorrow's sel' wears past, John,
And joy's a-coming fast, John,
The joy that's ay to last
    In the land o' the leal.

Sae dear's the joy was bought, John,
Sae free the battle fought, John,
That sinfu' man e'er brought
    To the land o' the leal.
O, dry your glistening e'e, John!
My saul langs to be free, John,
And angels beckon me
    To the land o' the leal.

O, haud ye leal and true, John!
Your day it's wearin' through, John,
And I'll welcome you
    To the land o' the leal.
Now fare-ye-weel, my ain John,
This warld's cares are vain, John,
We'll meet, and we'll be fain,
    In the land o' the leal.

Lady Nairne (1776–1845)

The Light of Other Days

Oft, in the stilly night,
    Ere slumber's chain has bound me,
Fond Memory brings the light
    Of other days around me:

The smiles, the tears
Of boyhood's years,
The words of love then spoken;
The eyes that shone,
Now dimm'd and gone,
The cheerful hearts now broken!
Thus, in the stilly night,
Ere slumber's chain has bound me,
Sad Memory brings the light
Of other days around me.

When I remember all
The friends, so link'd together,
I've seen around me fall
Like leaves in wintry weather,
I feel like one
Who treads alone
Some banquet-hall deserted,
Whose lights are fled,
Whose garlands dead,
And all but he departed!
Thus, in the stilly night,
Ere slumber's chain has bound me,
Sad Memory brings the light
Of other days around me.

THOMAS MOORE (1779–1852)

She dwelt among the Untrodden Ways

SHE dwelt among the untrodden ways
Beside the springs of Dove,
A Maid whom there were none to praise
And very few to love:

[434]

A violet by a mossy stone
   Half hidden from the eye!
Fair as a star, when only one
   Is shining in the sky.

She lived unknown, and few could know
   When Lucy ceased to be;
But she is in her grave, and oh,
   The difference to me!

       WILLIAM WORDSWORTH (1770–1850)

Rose Aylmer

AH, what avails the sceptred race!
   Ah, what the form divine!
What every virtue, every grace!
   Rose Aylmer, all were thine.

Rose Aylmer, whom these wakeful eyes
   May weep, but never see,
A night of memories and sighs
   I consecrate to thee.

       WALTER SAVAGE LANDOR (1775–1864)

His Books

MY days among the Dead are past;
   Around me I behold,
Where'er these casual eyes are cast,
   The mighty minds of old:
My never-failing friends are they,
With whom I converse day by day.

With them I take delight in weal
　　And seek relief in woe;
And while I understand and feel
　　How much to them I owe,
My cheeks have often been bedew'd
With tears of thoughtful gratitude.

My thoughts are with the Dead; with them
　　I live in long-past years,
Their virtues love, their faults condemn,
　　Partake their hopes and fears;
And from their lessons seek and find
Instruction with an humble mind.

My hopes are with the Dead; anon
　　My place with them will be,
And I with them shall travel on
　　Through all Futurity;
Yet leaving here a name, I trust,
That will not perish in the dust.

ROBERT SOUTHEY (1774–1843)

As Toilsome I wander'd Virginia's Woods

As toilsome I wander'd Virginia's woods,
To the music of rustling leaves kick'd by my feet, (for
　　'twas Autumn,)
I mark'd at the foot of a tree the grave of a soldier;
Mortally wounded he and buried on the retreat, (easily all
　　could I understand,)
The halt of a mid-day hour, when up! no time to lose—
　　yet this sign left,
On a tablet scrawl'd and nail'd on the tree by the grave,
Bold, cautious, true, and my loving comrade.

[436]

Long, long I muse, then on my way go wandering,
Many a changeful season to follow, and many a scene of
    life,
Yet at times through changeful season and scene, abrupt,
    alone, or in the crowded street,
Comes before me the unknown soldier's grave, comes the
    inscription rude in Virginia's woods,
Bold, cautious, true, and my loving comrade.

                WALT WHITMAN (1819–92)

O Captain ! My Captain !

O CAPTAIN! my Captain! our fearful trip is done,
The ship has weather'd every rack, the prize we sought is
    won,
The port is near, the bells I hear, the people all exulting,
While follow eyes the steady keel, the vessel grim and
    daring;
    But O heart! heart! heart!
      O the bleeding drops of red!
        Where on the deck my Captain lies,
          Fallen cold and dead.

O Captain! my Captain! rise up and hear the bells;
Rise up—for you the flag is flung—for you the bugle trills,
For you bouquets and ribbon'd wreaths—for you the
    shores a-crowding,
For you they call, the swaying mass, their eager faces
    turning;
    Here, Captain! dear father!
      This arm beneath your head!
        It is some dream that on the deck
          You've fallen cold and dead.

My Captain does not answer, his lips are pale and still,
My father does not feel my arm, he has no pulse nor will;
The ship is anchor'd safe and sound, its voyage closed and
      done,
From fearful trip the victor ship comes in with object
      won;
     Exult, O shores! and ring, O bells!
      But I, with mournful tread,
        Walk the deck my Captain lies,
          Fallen cold and dead.

WALT WHITMAN

Reconciliation

WORLD over all, beautiful as the sky,
Beautiful that war and all its deeds of carnage must in time
      be utterly lost,
That the hands of the sisters Death and Night incessantly
      softly wash again, and ever again, this soil'd world;
For my enemy is dead, a man divine as myself is dead,
I look where he lies white-faced and still in the coffin—I
      draw near,
Bend down and touch lightly with my lips the white face
      in the coffin.

WALT WHITMAN

A Sight in Camp in the Daybreak Grey and Dim

A SIGHT in camp in the daybreak grey and dim,
As from my tent I emerge so early sleepless,
As slow I walk in the cool fresh air the path near by the
      hospital tent,
Three forms I see on stretchers lying, brought out there
      untended lying,

Over each the blanket spread, ample brownish woollen
    blanket,
Grey and heavy blanket, folding, covering all.
Curious I halt and silent stand,
Then with light fingers I from the face of the nearest,
    the first, just lift the blanket:
Who are you, elderly man so gaunt and grim, with well-
    grey'd hair, and flesh all sunken about the eyes?
Who are you, my dear comrade?
Then to the second I step—and who are you, my child
    and darling?
Who are you, sweet boy with cheeks yet blooming?
Then to the third—a face nor child nor old, very calm, as
    of beautiful yellow-white ivory:
Young man, I think I know you—I think this face is the
    face of the Christ Himself,
Dead and divine and brother of all, and here again He lies.

WALT WHITMAN

Requiescat

STREW on her roses, roses,
    And never a spray of yew.
In quiet she reposes:
    Ah! would that I did too.

Her mirth the world required:
    She bathed it in smiles of glee.
But her heart was tired, tired,
    And now they let her be.

Her life was turning, turning,
    In mazes of heat and sound.
But for peace her soul was yearning,
    And now peace laps her round.

Her cabin'd, ample Spirit,
    It flutter'd and fail'd for breath.
To-night it doth inherit
    The vasty hall of Death.

MATTHEW ARNOLD (1822–88)

Requiem

UNDER the wide and starry sky
    Dig the grave and let me lie:
Glad did I live and gladly die,
    And I laid me down with a will.

This be the verse you grave for me:
    Here he lies where he long'd to be ;
Home is the sailor, home from sea,
    And the hunter home from the hill.

ROBERT LOUIS STEVENSON (1850–94)

An Epitaph

HERE lies a most beautiful lady,
    Light of step and heart was she;
I think she was the most beautiful lady
    That ever was in the West Country.
But beauty vanishes; beauty passes;
    However rare—rare it be;
And when I crumble, who will remember
    This lady of the West Country?

WALTER DE LA MARE (b. 1873)

'*Since Maurice died*'

I NEVER shall love the snow again
  Since Maurice died:
With corniced drift it blocked the lane,
And sheeted in a desolate plain
  The country side.

The trees with silvery rime bedight
  Their branches bare.
By day no sun appeared; by night
The hidden moon shed thievish light
  In the misty air.

We fed the birds that flew around
  In flocks to be fed:
No shelter in holly or brake they found.
The speckled thrush on the frozen ground
  Lay frozen and dead.

We skated on stream and pond; we cut
  The crinching snow
To Doric temple or Arctic hut;
We laughed and sang at nightfall, shut
  By the fireside glow.

Yet grudged we our keen delights before
  Maurice should come.
We said, In-door or out-of-door
We shall love life for a month or more,
  When he is home.

They brought him home; 'twas two days late
  For Christmas day:
Wrapped in white, in solemn state,
A flower in his hand, all still and straight
  Our Maurice lay.

And two days ere the year outgave
    We laid him low.
The best of us truly were not brave,
When we laid Maurice down in his grave
    Under the snow.

ROBERT BRIDGES (b. 1844)

The Stone

' AND will you cut a stone for him,
To set above his head?
And will you cut a stone for him—
A stone for him?' she said.

Three days before, a splintered rock
Had struck her lover dead—
Had struck him in the quarry dead,
Where, careless of the warning call,
He loitered, while the shot was fired—
A lively stripling, brave and tall,
And sure of all his heart desired . . .
A flash, a shock,
A rumbling fall . . .
And, broken 'neath the broken rock,
A lifeless heap, with face of clay,
And still as any stone he lay,
With eyes that saw the end of all.

I went to break the news to her:
And I could hear my own heart beat
With dread of what my lips might say;
But some poor fool had sped before;
And, flinging wide her father's door,
Had blurted out the news to her,

And struck her lover dead for her,
Had struck the girl's heart dead in her,
Had struck life, lifeless, at a word,
And dropped it at her feet:
Then hurried on his witless way,
Scarce knowing she had heard.

And when I came, she stood alone—
A woman, turned to stone:
And, though no word at all she said,
I knew that all was known.

Because her heart was dead,
She did not sigh nor moan.
His mother wept:
She could not weep.
Her lover slept:
She could not sleep.
Three days, three nights,
She did not stir:
Three days, three nights,
Were one to her,
Who never closed her eyes
From sunset to sunrise,
From dawn to evenfall—
Her tearless, staring eyes,
That, seeing naught, saw all.

The fourth night when I came from work,
I found her at my door.
'And will you cut a stone for him?'
She said: and spoke no more:

But followed me, as I went in,
And sank upon a chair;
And fixed her grey eyes on my face,
With still, unseeing stare.
And, as she waited patiently,
I could not bear to feel
Those still, grey eyes that followed me,
Those eyes that plucked the heart from me,
Those eyes that sucked the breath from me
And curdled the warm blood in me,
Those eyes that cut me to the bone,
And pierced my marrow like cold steel.

And so I rose, and sought a stone;
And cut it, smooth and square:
And, as I worked, she sat and watched,
Beside me, in her chair.
Night after night, by candlelight,
I cut her lover's name:
Night after night, so still and white,
And like a ghost she came;
And sat beside me, in her chair,
And watched with eyes aflame.

She eyed each stroke,
And hardly stirred:
She never spoke
A single word:
And not a sound or murmur broke
The quiet, save the mallet-stroke.

With still eyes ever on my hands,
With eyes that seemed to burn my hands,
My wincing, overwearied hands,

She watched, with bloodless lips apart,
And silent, indrawn breath:
And every stroke my chisel cut,
Death cut still deeper in her heart:
The two of us were chiselling,
Together, I and death.

And when at length the job was done,
And I had lain the mallet by,
As if, at last, her peace were won,
She breathed his name; and, with a sigh,
Passed slowly through the open door:
And never crossed my threshold more.

Next night I laboured late, alone,
To cut her name upon the stone.

                    WILFRID WILSON GIBSON (b. 1880)

Friends Beyond

WILLIAM Dewy, Tranter Reuben, Farmer Ledlow late
          at plough,
     Robert's kin, and John's, and Ned's,
And the Squire, and Lady Susan, lie in Mellstock church-
          yard now!

'Gone,' I call them, gone for good, that group of local
          hearts and heads;
     Yet at mothy curfew-tide,
And at midnight when the noon-heat breathes it back
          from walls and leads,

They've a way of whispering to me—fellow-wight who
          yet abide—
     In the muted, measured note
Of a ripple under archways, or a lone cave's stillicide:

Tranter] Carrier.   stillicide] fall of drops.

' We have triumphed: this achievement turns the bane to
          antidote,
     Unsuccesses to success,
Many thought-worn eves and morrows to a morrow free
     of thought.

' No more need we corn and clothing, feel of old terrestrial
          stress;
     Chill detraction stirs no sigh;
Fear of death has even bygone us: death gave all that we
     possess.'

W. D.—' Ye mid burn the old bass-viol that I set such
          value by.'
     Squire.—' You may hold the manse in fee,
You may wed my spouse, may let my children's memory
     of me die.'

Lady S.—' You may have my rich brocades, my laces;
          take each household key;
     Ransack coffer, desk, bureau;
Quiz the few poor treasures hid there, con the letters kept
     by me.'

Far.—' Ye mid zell my favourite heifer, ye mid let the
          charlock grow,
     Foul the grinterns, give up thrift.'
Far. Wife.—' If ye break my best blue china, children, I
          shan't care or ho.'

All.—' We've no wish to hear the tidings, how the people's
          fortunes shift;
     What your daily doings are;
Who are wedded, born, divided; if your lives beat slow or
     swift.

mid] may.   grinterns] compartments of a granary.   ho] heed.

' Curious not the least are we if our intents you make or
          mar,
     If you quire to our old tune,
If the City stage still passes, if the weirs still roar afar.'

—Thus, with very gods' composure, freed those crosses
          late and soon
     Which, in life, the Trine allow
(Why, none witteth), and ignoring all that haps beneath
          the moon,

William Dewy, Tranter Reuben, Farmer Ledlow late at
          plough,
     Robert's kin, and John's, and Ned's,
And the Squire, and Lady Susan, murmur mildly to me
          now.

                              THOMAS HARDY (b. 1840)

IX

The Wife of Usher's Well

THERE lived a wife at Usher's well,
    And a wealthy wife was she;
She had three stout and stalwart sons,
    And sent them o'er the sea.

They hadna been a week from her,
    A week but barely ane,
When word came to the carline wife
    That her three sons were gane.

They hadna been a week from her,
    A week but barely three,
When word came to the carline wife
    That her sons she'd never see.

[447]

' I wish the wind may never cease,
    Nor fashes in the flood,
Till my three sons come hame to me
    In earthly flesh and blood! '

It fell about the Martinmas,
    When nights are lang and mirk,
The carline wife's three sons came hame,
    And their hats were o' the birk.

It neither grew in syke nor ditch,
    Nor yet in ony sheugh;
But at the gates o' Paradise
    That birk grew fair eneugh.

' Blow up the fire, my maidens!
    Bring water from the well!
For a' my house shall feast this night,
    Since my three sons are well.'

And she has made to them a bed,
    She 's made it large and wide;
And she 's ta'en her mantle her about,
    Sat down at the bedside.

Up then crew the red, red cock,
    And up and crew the gray;
The eldest to the youngest said,
    ' 'Tis time we were away.'

The cock he hadna craw'd but once,
    And clapp'd his wings at a',
When the youngest to the eldest said,
    ' Brother, we must awa'.

fashes] troubles.   syke] marsh.   sheugh] trench.

' The cock doth craw, the day doth daw,
    The channerin' worm doth chide;
Gin we be miss'd out o' our place,
    A sair pain we maun bide.'

' Lie still, lie still but a little wee while,
    Lie still but if we may;
Gin my mother should miss us when she wakes,
    She'll go mad ere it be day.'

' Fare ye weel, my mother dear!
    Fareweel to barn and byre!
And fare ye weel, the bonny lass
    That kindles my mother's fire!'

ANONYMOUS (15th century?)

Rosabelle

O LISTEN, listen, ladies gay!
    No haughty feat of arms I tell;
Soft is the note, and sad the lay,
    That mourns the lovely Rosabelle.—

' Moor, moor the barge, ye gallant crew!
    And, gentle lady, deign to stay!
Rest thee in Castle Ravensheuch,
    Nor tempt the stormy firth to-day.

' The blackening wave is edged with white:
    To inch and rock the sea-mews fly;
The fishers have heard the Water-Sprite,
    Whose screams forebode that wreck is nigh.

' Last night the gifted Seer did view
    A wet shroud swathed round lady gay;
Then stay thee, Fair, in Ravensheuch:
    Why cross the gloomy firth to-day?'—

channerin'] fretting.

' 'Tis not because Lord Lindesay's heir
    To-night at Roslin leads the ball,
But that my ladye-mother there
    Sits lonely in her castle-hall.

' 'Tis not because the ring they ride,
    And Lindesay at the ring rides well,
But that my sire the wine will chide,
    If 'tis not fill'd by Rosabelle.'—

O'er Roslin all that dreary night
    A wondrous blaze was seen to gleam;
'Twas broader than the watch-fire's light,
    And redder than the bright moonbeam.

It glared on Roslin's castled rock,
    It ruddied all the copse-wood glen;
'Twas seen from Dryden's groves of oak,
    And seen from cavern'd Hawthornden.

Seem'd all on fire that chapel proud,
    Where Roslin's chiefs uncoffin'd lie,
Each Baron, for a sable shroud,
    Sheathed in his iron panoply.

Seem'd all on fire within, around,
    Deep sacristy and altar's pale;
Shone every pillar foliage-bound,
    And glimmer'd all the dead men's mail.

Blazed battlement and pinnet high,
    Blazed every rose-carved buttress fair—
So still they blaze, when fate is nigh
    The lordly line of high St. Clair.

There are twenty of Roslin's barons bold
    Lie buried within that proud chapelle;
Each one the holy vault doth hold—
    But the sea holds lovely Rosabelle!

[450]

And each St. Clair was buried there,
  With candle, with book, and with knell;
But the sea-caves rung, and the wild winds sung,
  The dirge of lovely Rosabelle.

                    SIR WALTER SCOTT (1771–1832)

Kilmeny

BONNIE Kilmeny gaed up the glen;
But it wasna to meet Duneira's men,
Nor the rosy monk of the isle to see,
For Kilmeny was pure as pure could be.
It was only to hear the yorlin sing,
And pu' the cress-flower round the spring;
The scarlet hypp and the hindberrye,
And the nut that hung frae the hazel tree;
For Kilmeny was pure as pure could be.
But lang may her minny look o'er the wa',
And lang may she seek i' the green-wood shaw;
Lang the laird o' Duneira blame,
And lang, lang greet or Kilmeny come hame!

When many a day had come and fled,
When grief grew calm, and hope was dead,
When mess for Kilmeny's soul had been sung,
When the bedesman had pray'd and the dead-bell rung,
Late, late in gloamin' when all was still,
When the fringe was red on the westlin hill,
The wood was sere, the moon i' the wane,
The reek o' the cot hung over the plain,
Like a little wee cloud in the world its lane;

yorlin] yellow-hammer.   hindberrye] raspberry.   greet] weep.

When the ingle low'd wi' an eiry leme,
Late, late in the gloamin' Kilmeny came hame!

.   .   .   .

And oh, her beauty was fair to see,
But still and steadfast was her e'e!
Such beauty bard may never declare,
For there was no pride nor passion there;
And the soft desire of maiden's e'en
In that mild face could never be seen.
Her seymar was the lily flower,
And her cheek the moss-rose in the shower;
And her voice like the distant melodye,
That floats along the twilight sea.
But she loved to raike the lanely glen,
And keepèd afar frae the haunts of men;
Her holy hymns unheard to sing,
To suck the flowers, and drink the spring.
But wherever her peaceful form appear'd,
The wild beasts of the hill were cheer'd;
The wolf play'd blythly round the field,
The lordly byson low'd and kneel'd;
The dun deer woo'd with manner bland,
And cower'd aneath her lily hand.
And when at even the woodlands rung,
When hymns of other worlds she sung
In ecstasy of sweet devotion,
Oh, then the glen was all in motion!
The wild beasts of the forest came,
Broke from their bughts and faulds the tame,
And goved around, charm'd and amazed;
Even the dull cattle croon'd and gazed,

ingle] hearth.   leme] glow.   seymar] vest.   raike] roam.
goved] stared.

And murmur'd and look'd with anxious pain
For something the mystery to explain.
The buzzard came with the throstle-cock;
The corby left her houf in the rock:
The blackbird alang wi' the eagle flew;
The hind came tripping o'er the dew;
The wolf and the kid their raike began,
And the tod, and the lamb, and the leveret ran;
The hawk and the hern attour them hung,
And the merle and the mavis forhooy'd their young;
And all in a peaceful ring were hurl'd;
It was like an eve in a sinless world!

When a month and a day had come and gane,
Kilmeny sought the green-wood wene;
There laid her down on the leaves sae green,
And Kilmeny on earth was never mair seen.
But oh, the words that fell from her mouth
Were words of wonder, and words of truth!
But all the land were in fear and dread,
For they kendna whether she was living or dead.
It wasna her hame, and she couldna remain;
She left this world of sorrow and pain,
And return'd to the land of thought again.

JAMES HOGG (1770–1835)

Kubla Khan

IN Xanadu did Kubla Khan
    A stately pleasure-dome decree:
Where Alph, the sacred river, ran
Through caverns measureless to man
    Down to a sunless sea.

corby] carrion-crow.   houf] haunt.   tod] fox.   attour]
over.   forhooy'd] forsook.   wene] bower.

So twice five miles of fertile ground
  With walls and towers were girdled round:
And there were gardens bright with sinuous rills
Where blossom'd many an incense-bearing tree;
And here were forests ancient as the hills,
Enfolding sunny spots of greenery.

But oh, that deep romantic chasm which slanted
Down the green hill athwart a cedarn cover!
A savage place! as holy and enchanted
As e'er beneath a waning moon was haunted
By woman wailing for her demon-lover!
And from this chasm, with ceaseless turmoil seething,
As if this earth in fast thick pants were breathing,
A mighty fountain momently was forced;
Amid whose swift half-intermitted burst
Huge fragments vaulted like rebounding hail,
Or chaffy grain beneath the thresher's flail:
And 'mid these dancing rocks at once and ever
It flung up momently the sacred river.
Five miles meandering with a mazy motion
Through wood and dale the sacred river ran,
Then reach'd the caverns measureless to man,
And sank in tumult to a lifeless ocean:
And 'mid this tumult Kubla heard from far
Ancestral voices prophesying war!

The shadow of the dome of pleasure
  Floated midway on the waves;
Where was heard the mingled measure
  From the fountain and the caves.
It was a miracle of rare device,
A sunny pleasure-dome with caves of ice!

A damsel with a dulcimer
    In a vision once I saw:
It was an Abyssinian maid,
And on her dulcimer she play'd,
    Singing of Mount Abora.
Could I revive within me
Her symphony and song,
To such a deep delight 'twould win me,
That with music loud and long
I would build that dome in air,
That sunny dome! those caves of ice!
And all who heard should see them there,
And all should cry, Beware! Beware!
His flashing eyes, his floating hair!
Weave a circle round him thrice,
    And close your eyes with holy dread,
    For he on honey-dew hath fed,
And drunk the milk of Paradise.

                SAMUEL TAYLOR COLERIDGE (1772–1834)

The Rime of the Ancient Mariner
PART I

IT is an ancient Mariner,
And he stoppeth one of three.
' By thy long grey beard and glittering eye,
Now wherefore stopp'st thou me?

The Bridegroom's doors are open'd wide,
And I am next of kin;
The guests are met, the feast is set:
May'st hear the merry din.'

An ancient Mariner meeteth three gallants bidden to a wedding-feast and detaineth one.

[455]

He holds him with his skinny hand,
' There was a ship,' quoth he.
' Hold off! unhand me, grey-beard loon!'
Eftsoons his hand dropt he.

The Wedding-
Guest is spell-
bound by the
eye of the old
seafaring man,
and constrained
to hear his tale.

He holds him with his glittering eye—
The Wedding-Guest stood still,
And listens like a three years' child:
The Mariner hath his will.

The Wedding-Guest sat on a stone:
He cannot choose but hear;
And thus spake on that ancient man,
The bright-eyed Mariner:

' The ship was cheer'd, the harbour clear'd,
Merrily did we drop
Below the kirk, below the hill,
Below the lighthouse top,

The Mariner
tells how the
ship sailed
southward with
a good wind
and fair
weather, till
it reached the
Line.

The Sun came up upon the left,
Out of the sea came he!
And he shone bright, and on the right
Went down into the sea.

Higher and higher every day,
Till over the mast at noon——'
The Wedding-Guest here beat his breast,
For he heard the loud bassoon.

The Wedding-
Guest heareth
the bridal
music; but the
Mariner con-
tinueth his tale.

The bride hath paced into the hall,
Red as a rose is she;
Nodding their heads before her goes
The merry minstrelsy.

The Wedding-Guest he beat his breast,
Yet he cannot choose but hear;
And thus spake on that ancient man,
The bright-eyed Mariner:

' And now the Storm-blast came, and he
Was tyrannous and strong:
He struck with his o'ertaking wings,
And chased us south along.

The ship drawn by a storm toward the South Pole.

With sloping masts and dipping prow,
As who pursued with yell and blow
Still treads the shadow of his foe,
And forward bends his head,
The ship drove fast, loud roar'd the blast,
And southward ay we fled.

And now there came both mist and snow
And it grew wondrous cold:
And ice, mast-high, came floating by,
As green as emerald.

And through the drifts the snowy clifts
Did send a dismal sheen:
Nor shapes of men nor beasts we ken—
The ice was all between.

The land of ice, and of fearful sounds, where no living thing was to be seen.

The ice was here, the ice was there,
The ice was all around:
It crack'd and growl'd, and roar'd and howl'd,
Like noises in a swound!

At length did cross an Albatross,
Thorough the fog it came;
As if it had been a Christian soul,
We hail'd it in God's name.

Till a great sea-bird, called the Albatross, came through the snow-fog, and was received with great joy and hospitality.

[457]

It ate the food it ne'er had eat,
And round and round it flew.
The ice did split with a thunder-fit;
The helmsman steer'd us through!

And lo! the Albatross proveth a bird of good omen, and followeth the ship as it returned northward through fog and floating ice.

And a good south wind sprung up behind;
The Albatross did follow,
And every day, for food or play,
Came to the mariners' hollo!

In mist or cloud, on mast or shroud,
It perch'd for vespers nine;
Whiles all the night, through fog-smoke white,
Glimmer'd the white moonshine.'

The ancient Mariner inhospitably killeth the pious bird of good omen.

' God save thee, ancient Mariner,
From the fiends, that plague thee thus!—
Why look'st thou so? '—' With my crossbow
I shot the Albatross.

PART II

'The Sun now rose upon the right:
Out of the sea came he,
Still hid in mist, and on the left
Went down into the sea.

And the good south wind still blew behind,
But no sweet bird did follow,
Nor any day for food or play
Came to the mariners' hollo!

And I had done a hellish thing,
And it would work 'em woe:
For all averr'd I had kill'd the bird
That made the breeze to blow.
Ah wretch! said they, the bird to slay
That made the breeze to blow!

His shipmates cry out against the ancient Mariner for killing the bird of good luck.

Nor dim nor red, like God's own head,
The glorious Sun uprist:
Then all averr'd I had kill'd the bird
That brought the fog and mist.
'Twas right, said they, such birds to slay,
That bring the fog and mist.

But when the fog cleared off, they justify the same, and thus make themselves accomplices in the crime.

The fair breeze blew, the white foam flew,
The furrow follow'd free;
We were the first that ever burst
Into that silent sea.

The fair breeze continues; the ship enters the Pacific Ocean, and sails northward, even till it reaches the Line.

Down dropt the breeze, the sails dropt down,
'Twas sad as sad could be;
And we did speak only to break
The silence of the sea!

The ship hath been suddenly becalmed.

All in a hot and copper sky,
The bloody Sun, at noon,
Right up above the mast did stand,
No bigger than the Moon.

Day after day, day after day,
We stuck, nor breath nor motion;
As idle as a painted ship
Upon a painted ocean.

And the Albatross begins to be avenged.

Water, water, everywhere,
And all the boards did shrink;
Water, water, everywhere,
Nor any drop to drink.

The very deep did rot: O Christ!
That ever this should be!
Yea, slimy things did crawl with legs
Upon the slimy sea.

About, about, in reel and rout
The death-fires danced at night;
The water, like a witch's oils,
Burnt green, and blue, and white.

A Spirit had followed them; one of the invisible inhabitants of this planet, neither departed souls nor angels; concerning whom the learned Jew, Josephus, and the Platonic Constantinopolitan, Michael Psellus, may be consulted. They are very numerous, and there is no climate or element without one or more.

And some in dreams assurèd were
Of the Spirit that plagued us so;
Nine fathom deep he had follow'd us
From the land of mist and snow.

And every tongue, through utter drought,
Was wither'd at the root;
We could not speak, no more than if
We had been choked with soot.

The shipmates in their sore distress, would fain throw the whole guilt on the ancient Mariner: in sign whereof they hang the dead sea-bird round his neck.

Ah! well-a-day! what evil looks
Had I from old and young!
Instead of the cross, the Albatross
About my neck was hung.

[460]

Part III

' There passed a weary time.   Each throat
Was parch'd, and glazed each eye.
A weary time! a weary time!
How glazed each weary eye!
When looking westward, I beheld
A something in the sky.

The ancient Mariner beholdeth a sign in the element afar off.

At first it seem'd a little speck,
And then it seem'd a mist;
It moved and moved, and took at last
A certain shape, I wist.

A speck, a mist, a shape, I wist!
And still it near'd and near'd:
As if it dodged a water-sprite,
It plung'd, and tack'd, and veer'd.

With throats unslaked, with black lips baked,
We could nor laugh nor wail;
Through utter drought all dumb we stood!
I bit my arm, I suck'd the blood,
And cried, " A sail! a sail! "

At its nearer approach, it seemeth him to be a ship; and at a dear ransom he freeth his speech from the bonds of thirst.

With throats unslaked, with black lips baked,
Agape they heard me call:
Gramercy! they for joy did grin,
And all at once their breath drew in,
As they were drinking all.

A flash of joy:

See! see! (I cried) she tacks no more!
Hither to work us weal—
Without a breeze, without a tide,
She steadies with upright keel!

And horror follows. For can it be a ship that comes onward without wind or tide?

The western wave was all aflame,
The day was wellnigh done!
Almost upon the western wave
Rested the broad, bright Sun;
When that strange shape drove suddenly
Betwixt us and the Sun.

It seemeth him but the skeleton of a ship.

And straight the Sun was fleck'd with bars
(Heaven's Mother send us grace!)
As if through a dungeon-grate he peer'd
With broad and burning face.

Alas! (thought I, and my heart beat loud)
How fast she nears and nears!
Are those her sails that glance in the Sun,
Like restless gossameres?

And its ribs are seen as bars on the face of the setting Sun. The Spectre-Woman and her Death-mate, and no other, on board the skeleton ship. Like vessel, like crew!

Are those her ribs through which the Sun
Did peer, as through a grate?
And is that Woman all her crew?
Is that a Death? and are there two?
Is Death that Woman's mate?

Her lips were red, her looks were free,
Her locks were yellow as gold:
Her skin was as white as leprosy,
The Nightmare Life-in-Death was she,
Who thicks man's blood with cold.

Death and Life-in-Death have diced for the ship's crew, and she (the latter) winneth the ancient Mariner.

The naked hulk alongside came,
And the twain were casting dice;
"The game is done! I've won! I've won!"
Quoth she, and whistles thrice.

[462]

The Sun's rim dips; the stars rush out:
At one stride comes the dark;
With far-heard whisper, o'er the sea,
Off shot the spectre-bark.

No twilight within the courts of the Sun.

We listen'd and look'd sideways up!
Fear at my heart, as at a cup,
My life-blood seem'd to sip!
The stars were dim, and thick the night,
The steersman's face by his lamp gleam'd
          white;
From the sails the dew did drip—
Till clomb above the eastern bar
The hornèd Moon, with one bright star
Within the nether tip.

At the rising of the Moon,

One after one, by the star-dogg'd Moon,
Too quick for groan or sigh,
Each turn'd his face with a ghastly pang,
And cursed me with his eye.

One after another,

Four times fifty living men
(And I heard nor sigh nor groan),
With heavy thump, a lifeless lump,
They dropp'd down one by one.

His shipmates drop down dead.

The souls did from their bodies fly—
They fled to bliss or woe!
And every soul, it pass'd me by
Like the whizz of my crossbow!'

But Life-in-Death begins her work on the ancient Mariner

Part IV

' I fear thee, ancient Mariner!
I fear thy skinny hand!
And thou art long, and lank, and brown,
As is the ribb'd sea-sand.

The Wedding-Guest feareth that a spirit is talking to him.

I fear thee and thy glittering eye,
And thy skinny hand so brown.'—
'Fear not, fear not, thou wedding guest!
This body dropt not down.

*But the an-
cient Mariner
assureth him
of his bodily
life, and pro-
ceedeth to re-
late his horrible
penance.*

Alone, alone, all, all alone,
Alone on a wide, wide sea!
And never a saint took pity on
My soul in agony.

*He despiseth
the creatures of
the calm.*

The many men, so beautiful!
And they all dead did lie:
And a thousand thousand slimy things
Lived on; and so did I.

*And envieth
that they
should live,
and so many
lie dead.*

I look'd upon the rotting sea,
And drew my eyes away;
I look'd upon the rotting deck,
And there the dead men lay.

I look'd to heaven, and tried to pray;
But or ever a prayer had gusht,
A wicked whisper came, and made
My heart as dry as dust.

I closed my lids, and kept them close,
And the balls like pulses beat;
For the sky and the sea, and the sea and the
    sky,
Lay like a load on my weary eye,
And the dead were at my feet.

*But the curse
liveth for him
in the eye of the
dead men.*

The cold sweat melted from their limbs,
Nor rot nor reek did they:
The look with which they look'd on me
Had never pass'd away.

An orphan's curse would drag to hell
A spirit from on high;
But oh! more horrible than that
Is the curse in a dead man's eye!
Seven days, seven nights, I saw that curse,
And yet I could not die.

The moving Moon went up the sky, *In his loneli-*
And nowhere did abide; *ness and*
fixedness he
Softly she was going up, *yearneth*
towards the
And a star or two beside— *journeying*
Moon, and the
stars that still
sojourn, yet still
move onward; and everywhere the blue sky belongs to them, and is their appointed
rest and their native country and their own natural homes, which they enter
unannounced, as lords that are certainly expected, and yet there is a silent joy
at their arrival.

Her beams bemock'd the sultry main,
Like April hoar-frost spread;
But where the ship's huge shadow lay,
The charmèd water burnt alway
A still and awful red.

Beyond the shadow of the ship, *By the light*
I watch'd the water-snakes: *of the Moon*
he beholdeth
They moved in tracks of shining white, *God's crea-*
And when they rear'd, the elfish light *tures of the*
great calm.
Fell off in hoary flakes.

Within the shadow of the ship
I watch'd their rich attire:
Blue, glossy green, and velvet black,
They coil'd and swam; and every track
Was a flash of golden fire.

O happy living things! no tongue
Their beauty might declare:
A spring of love gush'd from my heart,

And I bless'd them unaware:
Sure my kind saint took pity on me,
And I bless'd them unaware.

The selfsame moment I could pray;
And from my neck so free
The Albatross fell off, and sank
Like lead into the sea.

PART V

'O sleep! it is a gentle thing,
Beloved from pole to pole!
To Mary Queen the praise be given!
She sent the gentle sleep from Heaven,
That slid into my soul.

The silly buckets on the deck,
That had so long remain'd,
I dreamt that they were fill'd with dew;
And when I awoke, it rain'd.

My lips were wet, my throat was cold,
My garments all were dank;
Sure I had drunken in my dreams,
And still my body drank.

I moved, and could not feel my limbs:
I was so light—almost
I thought that I had died in sleep,
And was a blessèd ghost.

[466]

And soon I heard a roaring wind:
It did not come anear;
But with its sound it shook the sails,
That were so thin and sere.

He heareth
sounds and
seeth strange
sights and
commotions
in the sky and
the element.

The upper air burst into life;
And a hundred fire-flags sheen;
To and fro they were hurried about!
And to and fro, and in and out,
The wan stars danced between.

And the coming wind did roar more loud,
And the sails did sigh like sedge;
And the rain pour'd down from one black
          cloud;
The Moon was at its edge.

The thick black cloud was cleft, and still
The Moon was at its side;
Like waters shot from some high crag,
The lightning fell with never a jag,
A river steep and wide.

The loud wind never reach'd the ship,
Yet now the ship moved on!
Beneath the lightning and the Moon
The dead men gave a groan.

The bodies of
the ship's crew
are inspired,
and the ship
moves on ;

They groan'd, they stirr'd, they all uprose,
Nor spake, nor moved their eyes;
It had been strange, even in a dream,
To have seen those dead men rise.

[467]

The helmsman steer'd, the ship moved on;
Yet never a breeze up-blew;
The mariners all 'gan work the ropes,
Where they were wont to do;
They raised their limbs like lifeless tools—
We were a ghastly crew.

The body of my brother's son
Stood by me, knee to knee:
The body and I pull'd at one rope,
But he said naught to me.'

But not by
the souls of
the men, nor
by demons of
earth or middle
air, but by a
blessed troop
of angelic
spirits, sent
down by the
invocation of
the guardian
saint.

' I fear thee, ancient Mariner ! '
' Be calm, thou Wedding-Guest:
'Twas not those souls that fled in pain,
Which to their corses came again,
But a troop of spirits blest:

For when it dawn'd—they dropp'd their
arms,
And cluster'd round the mast;
Sweet sounds rose slowly through their
mouths,
And from their bodies pass'd.

Around, around, flew each sweet sound,
Then darted to the Sun;
Slowly the sounds came back again,
Now mix'd, now one by one.

Sometimes a-dropping from the sky
I heard the skylark sing;
Sometimes all little birds that are,
How they seem'd to fill the sea and air
With their sweet jargoning!

And now 'twas like all instruments,
Now like a lonely flute;
And now it is an angel's song,
That makes the Heavens be mute.

It ceased; yet still the sails made on
A pleasant noise till noon,
A noise like of a hidden brook
In the leafy month of June,
That to the sleeping woods all night
Singeth a quiet tune.

Till noon we quietly sail'd on,
Yet never a breeze did breathe:
Slowly and smoothly went the ship,
Moved onward from beneath.

Under the keel nine fathom deep,
From the land of mist and snow,
The Spirit slid: and it was he
That made the ship to go.
The sails at noon left off their tune,
And the ship stood still also.

The lonesome Spirit from the South Pole carries on the ship as far as the Line, in obedience to the angelic troop, but still requireth vengeance.

The Sun, right up above the mast,
Had fix'd her to the ocean:
But in a minute she 'gan stir,
With a short uneasy motion—
Backwards and forwards half her length
With a short uneasy motion.

Then like a pawing horse let go,
She made a sudden bound:
It flung the blood into my head,
And I fell down in a swound.

[469]

The Polar Spirit's fellow-demons, the invisible inhabitants of the element, take part in his wrong; and two of them relate, one to the other, that penance long and heavy for the ancient Mariner hath been accorded to the Polar Spirit, who returneth southward.

How long in that same fit I lay,
I have not to declare;
But ere my living life return'd,
I heard, and in my soul discern'd
Two voices in the air.

" Is it he ? " quoth one, " is this the man ?
By Him who died on cross,
With his cruel bow he laid full low
The harmless Albatross.

The Spirit who bideth by himself
In the land of mist and snow,
He loved the bird that loved the man
Who shot him with his bow."

The other was a softer voice,
As soft as honey-dew:
Quoth he, " The man hath penance done,
And penance more will do."

PART VI

First Voice :

' " But tell me, tell me ! speak again,
Thy soft response renewing—
What makes that ship drive on so fast ?
What is the Ocean doing ? "

Second Voice :

" Still as a slave before his lord,
The Ocean hath no blast;
His great bright eye most silently
Up to the Moon is cast—

[470]

If he may know which way to go;
For she guides him smooth or grim.
See, brother, see! how graciously
She looketh down on him."

First Voice :

" But why drives on that ship so fast,
Without or wave or wind ? "

The Mariner hath been cast into a trance ; for the angelic power causeth the vessel to drive northward faster than human life could endure.

Second Voice :

" The air is cut away before,
And closes from behind.

Fly, brother, fly! more high, more high!
Or we shall be belated:
For slow and slow that ship will go,
When the Mariner's trance is abated."

I woke, and we were sailing on
As in a gentle weather:
'Twas night, calm night, the Moon was
    high;
The dead men stood together.

The super-natural motion is retarded ; the Mariner awakes, and his penance begins anew.

All stood together on the deck,
For a charnel-dungeon fitter:
All fix'd on me their stony eyes,
That in the Moon did glitter.

The pang, the curse, with which they died,
Had never pass'd away:
I could not draw my eyes from theirs,
Nor turn them up to pray.

The curse is finally expiated.

And now this spell was snapt: once more
I viewed the ocean green,
And look'd far forth, yet little saw
Of what had else been seen—

Like one that on a lonesome road
Doth walk in fear and dread,
And having once turn'd round, walks on,
And turns no more his head;
Because he knows a frightful fiend
Doth close behind him tread.

But soon there breathed a wind on me,
Nor sound nor motion made:
Its path was not upon the sea,
In ripple or in shade.

It raised my hair, it fann'd my cheek
Like a meadow-gale of spring—
It mingled strangely with my fears,
Yet it felt like a welcoming.

Swiftly, swiftly flew the ship,
Yet she sail'd softly too:
Sweetly, sweetly blew the breeze—
On me alone it blew.

And the ancient Mariner beholdeth his native country.

O dream of joy! is this indeed
The lighthouse top I see?
Is this the hill? is this the kirk?
Is this mine own countree?

We drifted o'er the harbour-bar,
And I with sobs did pray—
O let me be awake, my God!
Or let me sleep alway.

The harbour-bay was clear as glass,
So smoothly it was strewn!
And on the bay the moonlight lay,
And the shadow of the Moon.

The rock shone bright, the kirk no less
That stands above the rock:
The moonlight steep'd in silentness
The steady weathercock.

And the bay was white with silent light,
Till rising from the same,
Full many shapes, that shadows were,
In crimson colours came.

The angelic spirits leave the dead bodies.

A little distance from the prow
Those crimson shadows were:
I turn'd my eyes upon the deck—
O Christ! what saw I there!

And appear in their own forms of light.

Each corse lay flat, lifeless and flat,
And, by the holy rood!
A man all light, a seraph-man,
On every corse there stood.

This seraph-band, each waved his hand:
It was a heavenly sight!
They stood as signals to the land,
Each one a lovely light;

This seraph-band, each waved his hand,
No voice did they impart—
No voice; but O, the silence sank
Like music on my heart.

But soon I heard the dash of oars,
I heard the Pilot's cheer;
My head was turn'd perforce away,
And I saw a boat appear.

The Pilot and the Pilot's boy,
I heard them coming fast:
Dear Lord in Heaven! it was a joy
The dead men could not blast.

I saw a third—I heard his voice:
It is the Hermit good!
He singeth loud his godly hymns
That he makes in the wood.
He'll shrieve my soul, he'll wash away
The Albatross's blood.

Part VII

The Hermit
of the Wood.

'This hermit good lives in that wood
Which slopes down to the sea.
How loudly his sweet voice he rears!
He loves to talk with marineres
That come from a far countree.

He kneels at morn, and noon, and eve—
He hath a cushion plump:
It is the moss that wholly hides
The rotted old oak-stump.

The skiff-boat near'd: I heard them talk,
" Why, this is strange, I trow!
Where are those lights so many and fair,
That signal made but now ? "

[474]

" Strange, by my faith ! " the Hermit said— Approacheth the ship with wonder.
" And they answer'd not our cheer !
The planks look warp'd ! and see those sails,
How thin they are and sere !
I never saw aught like to them,
Unless perchance it were

Brown skeletons of leaves that lag
My forest-brook along;
When the ivy-tod is heavy with snow,
And the owlet whoops to the wolf below,
That eats the she-wolf's young."

" Dear Lord ! it hath a fiendish look—
(The Pilot made reply)
I am a-fear'd."—" Push on, push on ! "
Said the Hermit cheerily.

The boat came closer to the ship,
But I nor spake nor stirr'd;
The boat came close beneath the ship,
And straight a sound was heard.

Under the water it rumbled on, The ship suddenly sinketh.
Still louder and more dread:
It reach'd the ship, it split the bay;
The ship went down like lead.

Stunn'd by that loud and dreadful sound, The ancient Mariner is saved in the Pilot's boat.
Which sky and ocean smote,
Like one that hath been seven days drown'd
My body lay afloat;
But swift as dreams, myself I found
Within the Pilot's boat.

Upon the whirl, where sank the ship,
The boat spun round and round;
And all was still, save that the hill
Was telling of the sound.

I moved my lips—the Pilot shriek'd
And fell down in a fit;
The holy Hermit raised his eyes,
And pray'd where he did sit.

I took the oars: the Pilot's boy,
Who now doth crazy go,
Laugh'd loud and long, and all the while
His eyes went to and fro.
" Ha! ha!" quoth he, " full plain I see
The Devil knows how to row."

And now, all in my own countree,
I stood on the firm land!
The Hermit stepp'd forth from the boat,
And scarcely he could stand.

The ancient Mariner earnestly entreateth the Hermit to shrieve him; and the penance of life falls on him.

" O shrieve me, shrieve me, holy man! "
The Hermit cross'd his brow.
" Say quick," quoth he, " I bid thee say—
What manner of man art thou? "

Forthwith this frame of mine was wrench'd
With a woful agony,
Which forced me to begin my tale;
And then it left me free.

And ever and anon throughout his future life an agony constraineth him to travel from land to land;

Since then, at an uncertain hour,
That agony returns:
And till my ghastly tale is told,
This heart within me burns.

I pass, like night, from land to land;
I have strange power of speech;
That moment that his face I see,
I know the man that must hear me:
To him my tale I teach.

What loud uproar bursts from that door!
The wedding-guests are there:
But in the garden-bower the bride
And bride-maids singing are:
And hark, the little vesper bell,
Which biddeth me to prayer!

O Wedding-Guest! this soul hath been
Alone on a wide, wide sea:
So lonely 'twas, that God Himself
Scarce seemèd there to be.

O sweeter than the marriage-feast,
'Tis sweeter far to me,
To walk together to the kirk
With a goodly company!—

To walk together to the kirk,
And all together pray,
While each to his great Father bends,
Old men, and babes, and loving friends,
And youths and maidens gay!

Farewell, farewell! but this I tell
To thee, thou Wedding-Guest!
He prayeth well, who loveth well
Both man and bird and beast.

And to teach,
by his own
example,
love and
reverence to
all things
that God
made and
loveth.

[477]

He prayeth best, who loveth best
All things both great and small;
For the dear God who loveth us,
He made and loveth all.'

The Mariner, whose eye is bright,
Whose beard with age is hoar,
Is gone: and now the Wedding-Guest
Turn'd from the bridegroom's door.

He went like one that hath been stunn'd,
And is of sense forlorn:
A sadder and a wiser man
He rose the morrow morn.

SAMUEL TAYLOR COLERIDGE

La Belle Dame sans Merci

' OH, what can ail thee, knight-at-arms,
    Alone and palely loitering?
The sedge is wither'd from the lake,
    And no birds sing.

' Oh, what can ail thee, knight-at-arms,
    So haggard and so woe-begone?
The squirrel's granary is full,
    And the harvest's done.

' I see a lily on thy brow
    With anguish moist and fever dew;
And on thy cheek a fading rose
    Fast withereth too.'

' I met a lady in the meads,
    Full beautiful—a faery's child;
Her hair was long, her foot was light,
    And her eyes were wild.

[478]

' I made a garland for her head,
   And bracelets too, and fragrant zone;
She look'd at me as she did love,
      And made sweet moan.

' I set her on my pacing steed
   And nothing else saw all day long,
For sideways would she lean, and sing
      A faery's song.

' She found me roots of relish sweet,
   And honey wild and manna dew,
And sure in language strange she said,
      " I love thee true! "

' She took me to her elfin grot,
   And there she wept and sigh'd full sore;
And there I shut her wild, wild eyes
      With kisses four.

' And there she lullèd me asleep,
   And there I dream'd—Ah! woe betide!
The latest dream I ever dream'd
      On the cold hill's side.

' I saw pale kings and princes too,
   Pale warriors, death-pale were they all;
Who cried—" La belle Dame sans Merci
      Hath thee in thrall! "

' I saw their starved lips in the gloam
   With horrid warning gapèd wide,
And I awoke and found me here
      On the cold hill's side.

[479]

' And this is why I sojourn here
 Alone and palely loitering,
Though the sedge is wither'd from the lake,
 And no birds sing.'

      JOHN KEATS (1795–1821)

The Lady of Shalott

PART I

ON either side the river lie
Long fields of barley and of rye,
That clothe the wold and meet the sky;
And thro' the field the road runs by
   To many-tower'd Camelot;
And up and down the people go,
Gazing where the lilies blow
Round an island there below,
   The island of Shalott.

Willows whiten, aspens quiver,
Little breezes dusk and shiver
Thro' the wave that runs for ever
By the island in the river
   Flowing down to Camelot.
Four gray walls, and four gray towers,
Overlook a space of flowers,
And the silent isle imbowers
   The Lady of Shalott.

By the margin, willow-veil'd,
Slide the heavy barges trail'd
By slow horses; and unhail'd
The shallop flitteth silken-sail'd
   Skimming down to Camelot:

But who hath seen her wave her hand?
Or at the casement seen her stand?
Or is she known in all the land,
      The Lady of Shalott?

Only reapers, reaping early
In among the bearded barley,
Hear a song that echoes cheerly
From the river winding clearly,
      Down to tower'd Camelot:
And by the moon the reaper weary,
Piling sheaves in uplands airy,
Listening, whispers ' 'Tis the fairy
      Lady of Shalott.'

PART II

There she weaves by night and day
A magic web with colours gay.
She has heard a whisper say,
A curse is on her if she stay
      To look down to Camelot.
She knows not what the curse may be,
And so she weaveth steadily,
And little other care hath she,
      The Lady of Shalott.

And moving thro' a mirror clear
That hangs before her all the year,
Shadows of the world appear.
There she sees the highway near
      Winding down to Camelot:

There the river eddy whirls,
And there the surly village-churls,
And the red cloaks of market girls,
   Pass onward from Shalott.

Sometimes a troop of damsels glad,
An abbot on an ambling pad,
Sometimes a curly shepherd-lad,
Or long-hair'd page in crimson clad,
   Goes by to tower'd Camelot;
And sometimes thro' the mirror blue
The knights come riding two and two:
She hath no loyal knight and true,
   The Lady of Shalott.

But in her web she still delights
To weave the mirror's magic sights,
For often thro' the silent nights
A funeral, with plumes and lights,
   And music, went to Camelot:
Or when the moon was overhead,
Came two young lovers lately wed;
' I am half sick of shadows,' said
   The Lady of Shalott.

Part III

A bow-shot from her bower-eaves,
He rode between the barley-sheaves,
The sun came dazzling thro' the leaves,
And flamed upon the brazen greaves
   Of bold Sir Lancelot.

A red-cross knight for ever kneel'd
To a lady in his shield,
That sparkled on the yellow field,
      Beside remote Shalott.

The gemmy bridle glitter'd free,
Like to some branch of stars we see
Hung in the golden Galaxy.
The bridle bells rang merrily
      As he rode down to Camelot:
And from his blazon'd baldric slung
A mighty silver bugle hung,
And as he rode his armour rung,
      Beside remote Shalott.

All in the blue unclouded weather
Thick-jewell'd shone the saddle-leather,
The helmet and the helmet-feather
Burn'd like one burning flame together,
      As he rode down to Camelot.
As often thro' the purple night,
Below the starry clusters bright,
Some bearded meteor, trailing light,
      Moves over still Shalott.

His broad clear brow in sunlight glow'd;
On burnish'd hooves his war-horse trode;
From underneath his helmet flow'd
His coal-black curls as on he rode,
      As he rode down to Camelot.
From the bank and from the river
He flash'd into the crystal mirror,
'Tirra lirra,' by the river
      Sang Sir Lancelot.

She left the web, she left the loom,
She made three paces thro' the room,
She saw the water-lily bloom,
She saw the helmet and the plume,
　　　　She look'd down to Camelot.
Out flew the web and floated wide;
The mirror crack'd from side to side;
'The curse is come upon me!' cried
　　　　The Lady of Shalott.

PART IV

In the stormy east-wind straining,
The pale yellow woods were waning,
The broad stream in his banks complaining,
Heavily the low sky raining
　　　　Over tower'd Camelot;
Down she came and found a boat
Beneath a willow left afloat,
And round about the prow she wrote
　　　　The Lady of Shalott.

And down the river's dim expanse—
Like some bold seer in a trance,
Seeing all his own mischance—
With a glassy countenance
　　　　Did she look to Camelot.
And at the closing of the day
She loosed the chain, and down she lay;
The broad stream bore her far away,
　　　　The Lady of Shalott.

Lying, robed in snowy white
That loosely flew to left and right—
The leaves upon her falling light—
Thro' the noises of the night
        She floated down to Camelot:
And as the boat-head wound along
The willowy hills and fields among,
They heard her singing her last song,
        The Lady of Shalott.

Heard a carol, mournful, holy,
Chanted loudly, chanted lowly,
Till her blood was frozen slowly,
And her eyes were darkened wholly,
        Turn'd to tower'd Camelot;
For ere she reach'd upon the tide
The first house by the water-side,
Singing in her song she died,
        The Lady of Shalott.

Under tower and balcony,
By garden-wall and gallery,
A gleaming shape she floated by,
Dead-pale between the houses high,
        Silent into Camelot.
Out upon the wharfs they came,
Knight and burgher, lord and dame,
And round the prow they read her name,
        The Lady of Shalott.

Who is this? and what is here?
And in the lighted palace near
Died the sound of royal cheer;
And they cross'd themselves for fear,
        All the knights at Camelot:

But Lancelot mused a little space;
He said, ' She has a lovely face;
God in His mercy lend her grace,
    The Lady of Shalott.'

ALFRED, LORD TENNYSON (1809–92)

Morte d'Arthur

So all day long the noise of battle roll'd
Among the mountains by the winter sea;
Until King Arthur's table, man by man,
Had fall'n in Lyonness about their Lord,
King Arthur: then, because his wound was deep,
The bold Sir Bedivere uplifted him,
Sir Bedivere, the last of all his knights,
And bore him to a chapel nigh the field,
A broken chancel with a broken cross,
That stood on a dark strait of barren land.
On one side lay the Ocean, and on one
Lay a great water, and the moon was full.
    Then spake King Arthur to Sir Bedivere:
' The sequel of to-day unsolders all
The goodliest fellowship of famous knights
Whereof this world holds record. Such a sleep
They sleep—the men I loved. I think that we
Shall never more, at any future time,
Delight our souls with talk of knightly deeds,
Walking about the gardens and the halls
Of Camelot, as in the days that were.
I perish by this people which I made,—
Tho' Merlin sware that I should come again
To rule once more—but let what will be, be,

I am so deeply smitten thro' the helm
That without help I cannot last till morn.
Thou therefore take my brand Excalibur,
Which was my pride: for thou rememberest how
In those old days, one summer noon, an arm
Rose up from out the bosom of the lake,
Clothed in white samite, mystic, wonderful,
Holding the sword—and how I row'd across
And took it, and have worn it, like a king:
And, wheresoever I am sung or told
In aftertime, this also shall be known:
But now delay not: take Excalibur,
And fling him far into the middle mere:
Watch what thou seëst, and lightly bring me word.'

    To him replied the bold Sir Bedivere:
' It is not meet, Sir King, to leave thee thus,
Aidless, alone, and smitten thro' the helm.
A little thing may harm a wounded man.
Yet I thy hest will all perform at full,
Watch what I see, and lightly bring thee word.'

    So saying, from the ruin'd shrine he stept
And in the moon athwart the place of tombs,
Where lay the mighty bones of ancient men,
Old knights, and over them the sea-wind sang
Shrill, chill, with flakes of foam.   He, stepping down
By zig-zag paths, and juts of pointed rock,
Came on the shining levels of the lake.

    There drew he forth the brand Excalibur,
And o'er him, drawing it, the winter moon,
Brightening the skirts of a long cloud, ran forth
And sparkled keen with frost against the hilt:
For all the haft twinkled with diamond sparks,
Myriads of topaz-lights, and jacinth-work

Of subtlest jewellery. He gazed so long
That both his eyes were dazzled, as he stood,
This way and that dividing the swift mind,
In act to throw: but at the last it seem'd
Better to leave Excalibur conceal'd
There in the many-knotted waterflags,
That whistled stiff and dry about the marge.
So strode he back slow to the wounded king.

Then spake King Arthur to Sir Bedivere:
' Hast thou perform'd my mission which I gave?
What is it thou hast seen? or what hast heard?'

And answer made the bold Sir Bedivere:
' I heard the ripple washing in the reeds,
And the wild water lapping on the crag.'

To whom replied King Arthur, faint and pale:
' Thou hast betray'd thy nature and thy name,
Not rendering true answer, as beseem'd
Thy feälty, nor like a noble knight:
For surer sign had follow'd, either hand,
Or voice, or else a motion of the mere.
This is a shameful thing for men to lie.
Yet now, I charge thee, quickly go again
As thou art lief and dear, and do the thing
I bad thee, watch, and lightly bring me word.'

Then went Sir Bedivere the second time
Across the ridge, and paced beside the mere,
Counting the dewy pebbles, fix'd in thought;
But when he saw the wonder of the hilt,
How curiously and strangely chased, he smote
His palms together, and he cried aloud:

' And if indeed I cast the brand away,
Surely a precious thing, one worthy note,
Should thus be lost for ever from the earth,

[488]

Which might have pleased the eyes of many men,
What good should follow this, if this were done?
What harm, undone? deep harm to disobey,
Seeing obedience is the bond of rule.
Were it well to obey, then, if a king demand
An act unprofitable, against himself?
The King is sick, and knows not what he does.
What record, or what relic of my lord
Should be to aftertime, but empty breath
And rumours of a doubt? but were this kept,
Stored in some treasure-house of mighty kings,
Some one might show it at a joust of arms,
Saying, " King Arthur's sword, Excalibur,
Wrought by the lonely maiden of the Lake.
Nine years she wrought it, sitting in the deeps
Upon the hidden bases of the hills."
So might some old man speak in the aftertime
To all the people, winning reverence.
But now much honour and much fame were lost.'

　　So spake he, clouded with his own conceit,
And hid Excalibur the second time,
And so strode back slow to the wounded King.

　　Then spoke King Arthur, breathing heavily:
' What is it thou hast seen? or what hast heard?'

　　And answer made the bold Sir Bedivere:
' I heard the water lapping on the crag,
And the long ripple washing in the reeds.'

　　To whom replied King Arthur, much in wrath:
' Ah, miserable and unkind, untrue,
Unknightly, traitor-hearted! Woe is me!
Authority forgets a dying king,
Laid widow'd of the power in his eye
That bow'd the will. I see thee what thou art,

[489]

For thou, the latest-left of all my knights,
In whom should meet the offices of all,
Thou wouldst betray me for the precious hilt;
Either from lust of gold, or like a girl
Valuing the giddy pleasure of the eyes.
Yet, for a man may fail in duty twice,
And the third time may prosper, get thee hence:
But, if thou spare to fling Excalibur,
I will arise and slay thee with my hands.'

Then quickly rose Sir Bedivere, and ran,
And, leaping down the ridges lightly, plunged
Among the bulrush-beds, and clutch'd the sword,
And strongly wheel'd and threw it.   The great brand
Made lightnings in the splendour of the moon,
And flashing round and round, and whirl'd in an arch,
Shot like a streamer of the northern morn,
Seen where the moving isles of winter shock
By night, with noises of the northern sea.
So flash'd and fell the brand Excalibur:
But ere he dipt the surface, rose an arm
Clothed in white samite, mystic, wonderful,
And caught him by the hilt, and brandish'd him
Three times, and drew him under in the mere.
And lightly went the other to the King.

Then spoke King Arthur, drawing thicker breath:
' Now see I by thine eyes that this is done.
Speak out: what is it thou hast heard, or seen?'

And answer made the bold Sir Bedivere:
' Sir King, I closed mine eyelids, lest the gems
Should blind my purpose, for I never saw,
Nor shall see, here or elsewhere, till I die,
Not tho' I live three lives of mortal men,
So great a miracle as yonder hilt.

[490]

Then with both hands I flung him, wheeling him;
But when I look'd again, behold an arm,
Clothed in white samite, mystic, wonderful,
That caught him by the hilt, and brandish'd him
Three times, and drew him under in the mere.'

And answer made King Arthur, breathing hard;
' My end draws nigh; 'tis time that I were gone.
Make broad thy shoulders to receive my weight,
And bear me to the margin; yet I fear
My wound hath taken cold, and I shall die.'

So saying, from the pavement he half rose,
Slowly, with pain, reclining on his arm,
And looking wistfully with wide blue eyes
As in a picture.   Him Sir Bedivere
Remorsefully regarded thro' his tears,
And would have spoken, but he found not words,
Then took with care, and kneeling on one knee,
O'er both his shoulders drew the languid hands,
And rising bore him thro' the place of tombs.

But, as he walk'd, King Arthur panted hard,
Like one that feels a nightmare on his bed
When all the house is mute.   So sigh'd the King,
Muttering and murmuring at his ear, ' Quick, quick!
I fear it is too late, and I shall die.'
But the other swiftly strode from ridge to ridge,
Clothed with his breath, and looking, as he walk'd,
Larger than human on the frozen hills.
He heard the deep behind him, and a cry
Before.   His own thought drove him, like a goad.
Dry clash'd his harness in the icy caves
And barren chasms, and all to left and right
The bare black cliff clang'd round him, as he based
His feet on juts of slippery crag that rang

Sharp-smitten with the dint of armèd heels—
And on a sudden, lo! the level lake,
And the long glories of the winter moon.

Then saw they how there hove a dusky barge,
Dark as a funeral scarf from stem to stern,
Beneath them; and descending they were ware
That all the decks were dense with stately forms
Black-stoled, black-hooded, like a dream—by these
Three Queens with crowns of gold—and from them rose
A cry that shiver'd to the tingling stars,
And, as it were one voice, an agony
Of lamentation, like a wind, that shrills
All night in a waste land, where no one comes,
Or hath come, since the making of the world.

Then murmur'd Arthur, ' Place me in the barge,'
And to the barge they came.   There those three Queens
Put forth their hands, and took the King, and wept.
But she, that rose the tallest of them all
And fairest, laid his head upon her lap,
And loosed the shatter'd casque, and chafed his hands,
And call'd him by his name, complaining loud,
And dropping bitter tears against his brow
Striped with dark blood: for all his face was white
And colourless, and like the wither'd moon
Smote by the fresh beam of the springing east;
And all his greaves and cuisses dash'd with drops
Of onset; and the light and lustrous curls—
That made his forehead like a rising sun
High from the daïs-throne—were parch'd with dust;
Or, clotted into points and hanging loose,
Mix'd with the knightly growth that fringed his lips.
So like a shatter'd column lay the King;
Not like that Arthur who, with lance in rest,

From spur to plume a star of tournament,
Shot thro' the lists at Camelot, and charged
Before the eyes of ladies and of kings.

  Then loudly cried the bold Sir Bedivere:
'Ah! my Lord Arthur, whither shall I go?
Where shall I hide my forehead and my eyes?
For now I see the true old times are dead,
When every morning brought a noble chance,
And every chance brought out a noble knight.
Such times have been not since the light that led
The holy Elders with the gift of myrrh.
But now the whole ROUND TABLE is dissolved
Which was an image of the mighty world;
And I, the last, go forth companionless,
And the days darken round me, and the years,
Among new men, strange faces, other minds.'

  And slowly answer'd Arthur from the barge:
'The old order changeth, yielding place to new,
And God fulfils Himself in many ways,
Lest one good custom should corrupt the world.
Comfort thyself: what comfort is in me?
I have lived my life, and that which I have done
May He within Himself make pure! but thou,
If thou shouldst never see my face again,
Pray for my soul.   More things are wrought by prayer
Than this world dreams of.   Wherefore, let thy voice
Rise like a fountain for me night and day.
For what are men better than sheep or goats
That nourish a blind life within the brain,
If, knowing God, they lift not hands of prayer
Both for themselves and those who call them friend?
For so the whole round earth is every way
Bound by gold chains about the feet of God.

But now farewell. I am going a long way
With these thou seëst—if indeed I go—
(For all my mind is clouded with a doubt)
To the island-valley of Avilion;
Where falls not hail, or rain, or any snow,
Nor ever wind blows loudly; but it lies
Deep-meadow'd, happy, fair with orchard-lawns
And bowery hollows crown'd with summer sea,
Where I will heal me of my grievous wound.'
  So said he, and the barge with oar and sail
Moved from the brink, like some full-breasted swan
That, fluting a wild carol ere her death,
Ruffles her pure cold plume, and takes the flood
With swarthy webs. Long stood Sir Bedivere
Revolving many memories, till the hull
Look'd one black dot against the verge of dawn,
And on the mere the wailing died away.

ALFRED, LORD TENNYSON.

The Listeners

' Is there anybody there?' said the Traveller,
    Knocking on the moonlit door;
And his horse in the silence champed the grasses
    Of the forest's ferny floor:
And a bird flew up out of the turret,
    Above the Traveller's head:
And he smote upon the door again a second time;
    ' Is there anybody there?' he said.
But no one descended to the Traveller;
    No head from the leaf-fringed sill
Lean'd over and look'd into his grey eyes,
    Where he stood perplexed and still.

[494]

But only a host of phantom listeners
    That dwelt in the lone house then
Stood listening in the quiet of the moonlight
    To that voice from the world of men:
Stood thronging the faint moonbeams on the dark stair,
    That goes down to the empty hall,
Hearkening in an air stirred and shaken
    By the lonely Traveller's call.
And he felt in his heart their strangeness,
    Their stillness answering his cry,
While his horse moved, cropping the dark turf,
    'Neath the starred and leafy sky;
For he suddenly smote on the door, even
    Louder, and lifted his head:—
' Tell them I came, and no one answered,
    That I kept my word,' he said.
Never the least stir made the listeners,
    Though every word he spake
Fell echoing through the shadowiness of the still house
    From the one man left awake:
Ay, they heard his foot upon the stirrup,
    And the sound of iron on stone,
And how the silence surged softly backward,
    When the plunging hoofs were gone.

                  WALTER DE LA MARE (b. 1873)

Flannan Isle

  ' THOUGH three men dwell on Flannan Isle
  To keep the lamp alight,
  As we steered under the lee, we caught
  No glimmer through the night.'
          [495]

A passing ship at dawn had brought
The news; and quickly we set sail,
To find out what strange thing might ail
The keepers of the deep-sea light.

The Winter day broke blue and bright,
With glancing sun and glancing spray,
While o'er the swell our boat made way,
As gallant as a gull in flight.

But as we neared the lonely Isle,
And looked up at the naked height,
And saw the lighthouse towering white,
With blinded lantern, that all night
Had never shot a spark
Of comfort through the dark,
So ghostly in the cold sunlight
It seemed, that we were struck the while
With wonder all too dread for words.

And as into the tiny creek
We stole beneath the hanging crag,
We saw three queer, black, ugly birds—
Too big, by far, in my belief,
For cormorant or shag—
Like seamen sitting bolt-upright
Upon a half-tide reef:
But, as we neared, they plunged from sight,
Without a sound, or spurt of white.

And still too mazed to speak,
We landed; and made fast the boat;
And climbed the track in single file,
Each wishing he were safe afloat,

On any sea, however far,
So it be far from Flannan Isle:
And still we seemed to climb, and climb,
As though we'd lost all count of time,
And so must climb for evermore.
Yet, all too soon, we reached the door—
The black, sun-blistered lighthouse-door,
That gaped for us ajar.

As, on the threshold, for a spell,
We paused, we seemed to breathe the smell
Of limewash and of tar,
Familiar as our daily breath,
As though 'twere some strange scent of death:
And so, yet wondering, side by side,
We stood a moment, still tongue-tied:
And each with black foreboding eyed
The door, ere we should fling it wide,
To leave the sunlight for the gloom:
Till, plucking courage up, at last,
Hard on each other's heels we passed,
Into the living-room.

Yet, as we crowded through the door,
We only saw a table, spread
For dinner, meat and cheese and bread;
But, all untouched; and no one there:
As though, when they sat down to eat,
Ere they could even taste,
Alarm had come; and they in haste
Had risen and left the bread and meat:
For at the table-head a chair
Lay tumbled on the floor.

We listened; but we only heard
The feeble cheeping of a bird
That starved upon its perch:
And, listening still, without a word,
We set about our hopeless search.

We hunted high, we hunted low;
And soon ransacked the empty house;
Then o'er the Island, to and fro,
We ranged, to listen and to look
In every cranny, cleft or nook
That might have hid a bird or mouse:
But, though we searched from shore to shore,
We found no sign in any place:
And soon again stood face to face
Before the gaping door:
And stole into the room once more
As frightened children steal.

Ay: though we hunted high and low,
And hunted everywhere,
Of the three men's fate we found no trace
Of any kind in any place,
But a door ajar, and an untouched meal,
And an overtoppled chair.

And as we listened in the gloom
Of that forsaken living-room—
A chill clutch on our breath—
We thought how ill-chance came to all
Who kept the Flannan Light:
And how the rock had been the death
Of many a likely lad:
How six had come to a sudden end,
And three had gone stark mad:

And one whom we'd all known as friend
Had leapt from the lantern one still night,
And fallen dead by the lighthouse wall:
And long we thought
On the three we sought,
And of what might yet befall.

Like curs a glance has brought to heel,
We listened, flinching there:
And looked, and looked, on the untouched meal,
And the overtoppled chair.

We seemed to stand for an endless while,
Though still no word was said,
Three men alive on Flannan Isle,
Who thought on three men dead.

WILFRID WILSON GIBSON (b. 1880)

Night-Errantry

THREE long breaths of the blessèd night
And I am fast asleep;
No need to read by candle-light
Or count a flock of sheep.

Deep, deep I lie as any dead,
Save my breath comes and goes;
The holy dark is like a bed
With violet curtains close.

And while enfolded I lie there
Until the dawn of day,
My body is the prisoner,
My soul slips out to play.

[499]

A-tiptoe on the window-sill
He listens like a mouse,
The calling wind blows from the hill
And circles round the house.

Above the voices of the town
It whispers in the tree,
And brings the message of the Down:
'Tis there my soul would be.

Then while enchain'd my body lies
Like a dead man in grave,
Thither on trackless feet he hies,
On wings that make no wave.

The dawn comes out in cold gray sark
And finds him flitting there
Among the creatures of the dark,
Vixen and brock and hare.

O wild white face that's none of mine,
O eager eyes unknown,
What will you do with Proserpine,
And what shall I, alone?

O flying feet, O naked sides,
O tresses flowing free,
And are you his that all day bides
So soberly in me?

The sun streams up behind the hill
And strikes the window-pane;
The empty land lies hot and still,
And I am I again.

MAURICE HEWLETT (1861–1923)

brock] badger.

[500]

X

Preparations

YET if His Majesty, our sovereign lord,
Should of his own accord
Friendly himself invite,
And say ' I'll be your guest to-morrow night,'
How should we stir ourselves, call and command
All hands to work! ' Let no man idle stand!

' Set me fine Spanish tables in the hall;
See they be fitted all;
Let there be room to eat
And order taken that there want no meat.
See every sconce and candlestick made bright,
That without tapers they may give a light.

' Look to the presence: Are the carpets spread,
The dazie o'er the head,
The cushions in the chairs,
And all the candles lighted on the stairs?
Perfume the chambers, and in any case
Let each man give attendance in his place!'

Thus, if the king were coming, would we do;
And 'twere good reason too;
For 'tis a duteous thing
To show all honour to an earthly king,
And after all our travail and our cost,
So he be pleased, to think no labour lost.

dazie] canopy.
[501]

But at the coming of the King of Heaven
All's set at six and seven;
We wallow in our sin,
Christ cannot find a chamber in the inn.
We entertain Him always like a stranger,
And, as at first, still lodge Him in the manger.

ANONYMOUS (17th century)

Love

LOVE bade me welcome; yet my soul drew back,
    Guilty of dust and sin.
But quick-eyed Love, observing me grow slack
    From my first entrance in,
Drew nearer to me, sweetly questioning
    If I lack'd anything.

' A guest,' I answer'd, ' worthy to be here: '
    Love said, ' You shall be he.'
' I, the unkind, ungrateful? Ah, my dear,
    I cannot look on thee.'
Love took my hand and smiling did reply,
    ' Who made the eyes but I?'

' Truth, Lord; but I have marr'd them: let my shame
    Go where it doth deserve.'
' And know you not,' says Love, ' Who bore the blame?'
    ' My dear, then I will serve.'
' You must sit down,' says Love, ' and taste my meat.'
    So I did sit and eat.

GEORGE HERBERT (1593-1633)

Easter

I GOT me flowers to straw Thy way,
  I got me boughs off many a tree;
But Thou wast up by break of day,
  And brought'st Thy sweets along with Thee.

Yet though my flowers be lost, they say
  A heart can never come too late;
Teach it to sing Thy praise this day,
  And then this day my life shall date.

GEORGE HERBERT

Virtue

SWEET day, so cool, so calm, so bright!
The bridal of the earth and sky—
The dew shall weep thy fall to-night;
      For thou must die.

Sweet rose, whose hue angry and brave
Bids the rash gazer wipe his eye,
Thy root is ever in its grave,
      And thou must die.

Sweet spring, full of sweet days and roses,
A box where sweets compacted lie,
My music shows ye have your closes,
      And all must die.

Only a sweet and virtuous soul,
Like season'd timber, never gives;
But though the whole world turn to coal,
      Then chiefly lives.

GEORGE HERBERT

[503]

Friends departed

THEY are all gone into the world of light!
    And I alone sit ling'ring here;
Their very memory is fair and bright,
      And my sad thoughts doth clear.

It glows and glitters in my cloudy breast,
    Like stars upon some gloomy grove,
Or those faint beams in which this hill is drest
      After the sun's remove.

I see them walking in an air of glory,
    Whose light doth trample on my days:
My days, which are at best but dull and hoary,
      Mere glimmering and decays.

O holy Hope! and high Humility,
    High as the heavens above!
These are your walks, and you have show'd them me,
      To kindle my cold love.

Dear, beauteous Death! the jewel of the Just,
    Shining nowhere, but in the dark;
What mysteries do lie beyond thy dust,
      Could man outlook that mark!

He that hath found some fledged bird's nest may know,
    At first sight, if the bird be flown;
But what fair well or grove he sings in now,
      That is to him unknown.

And yet as Angels in some brighter dreams
    Call to the soul, when man doth sleep:
So some strange thoughts transcend our wonted themes,
      And into glory peep.

[504]

If a star were confined into a tomb,
    Her captive flames must needs burn there;
But when the hand that lock'd her up gives room,
    She'll shine through all the sphere.

O Father of eternal life, and all
    Created glories under Thee!
Resume Thy spirit from this world of thrall
    Into true liberty.

Either disperse these mists, which blot and fill
    My perspective still as they pass:
Or else remove me hence unto that hill,
    Where I shall need no glass.

HENRY VAUGHAN (1622–95)

The Retreat

HAPPY those early days, when I
Shined in my Angel-infancy!
Before I understood this place
Appointed for my second race,
Or taught my soul to fancy aught
But a white celestial thought:
When yet I had not walk'd above
A mile or two from my first Love,
And looking back—at that short space—
Could see a glimpse of His bright face:
When on some gilded cloud, or flow'r,
My gazing soul would dwell an hour,
And in those weaker glories spy
Some shadows of eternity:

[505]

Before I taught my tongue to wound
My Conscience with a sinful sound,
Or had the black art to dispense
A several sin to ev'ry sense,
But felt through all this fleshly dress
Bright shoots of everlastingness.

O how I long to travel back,
And tread again that ancient track!
That I might once more reach that plain
Where first I left my glorious train;
From whence th' enlighten'd spirit sees
That shady City of Palm-trees.
But ah! my soul with too much stay
Is drunk, and staggers in the way!
Some men a forward motion love,
But I by backward steps would move;
And when this dust falls to the urn,
In that state I came, return.

HENRY VAUGHAN

On the Morning of Christ's Nativity

THIS is the month, and this the happy morn,
Wherein the Son of Heaven's eternal King,
Of wedded maid and virgin mother born,
Our great redemption from above did bring;
For so the holy sages once did sing,
    That He our deadly forfeit should release,
And with His Father work us a perpetual peace.

That glorious Form, that Light unsufferable,
And that far-beaming blaze of Majesty,
Wherewith He wont at Heaven's high council-table
To sit the midst of Trinal Unity,
He laid aside; and here with us to be
    Forsook the courts of everlasting day,
And chose with us a darksome house of mortal clay.

Say, Heavenly Muse, shall not thy sacred vein
Afford a present to the Infant God?
Hast thou no verse, no hymn, or solemn strain,
To welcome Him to this His new abode,
Now while the Heaven, by the Sun's team untrod,
    Hath took no print of the approaching light,
And all the spangled host keep watch in squadrons bright?

See how from far upon the eastern road
The star-led wizards haste with odours sweet!
O run, prevent them with thy humble ode,
And lay it lowly at His blessèd feet;
Have thou the honour first thy Lord to greet,
    And join thy voice unto the angel quire,
From out His secret altar touch'd with hallow'd fire.

THE HYMN

IT was the winter wild,
While the Heaven-born Child
    All meanly wrapt in the rude manger lies;
Nature in awe to Him
Had doff'd her gaudy trim,
    With her great Master so to sympathize:
It was no season then for her
To wanton with the sun her lusty paramour.

Only with speeches fair
She woos the gentle air
    To hide her guilty front with innocent snow,
And on her naked shame,
Pollute with sinful blame,
    The saintly veil of maiden white to throw,
Confounded, that her Maker's eyes
Should look so near upon her foul deformities.

But He her fears to cease
Sent down the meek-eyed Peace;
    She crown'd with olive green came softly sliding
Down through the turning sphere,
His ready harbinger,
    With turtle wing the amorous clouds dividing,
And waving wide her myrtle wand,
She strikes a universal peace through sea and land.

No war or battle's sound
Was heard the world around,
    The idle spear and shield were high uphung;
The hookèd chariot stood
Unstain'd with hostile blood,
    The trumpet spake not to the armèd throng,
And kings sat still with awful eye,
As if they surely knew their sovran Lord was by.

But peaceful was the night
Wherein the Prince of Light
    His reign of peace upon the earth began:
The winds, with wonder whist,
Smoothly the waters kiss'd,
    Whispering new joys to the mild Ocean,
Who now hath quite forgot to rave,
While birds of calm sit brooding on the charmèd wave.

The stars with deep amaze
Stand fix'd in steadfast gaze,
   Bending one way their precious influence,
And will not take their flight,
For all the morning light,
   Or Lucifer that often warn'd them thence:
But in their glimmering orbs did glow,
Until their Lord Himself bespake, and bid them go.

And though the shady gloom
Had given day her room,
   The sun himself withheld his wonted speed,
And hid his head for shame,
As his inferior flame
   The new-enlighten'd world no more should need;
He saw a greater Sun appear
Than his bright throne or burning axletree could bear.

The shepherds on the lawn,
Or ere the point of dawn,
   Sat simply chatting in a rustic row;
Full little thought they than
That the mighty Pan
   Was kindly come to live with them below;
Perhaps their loves, or else their sheep,
Was all that did their silly thoughts so busy keep.

When such music sweet
Their hearts and ears did greet,
   As never was by mortal finger strook,
Divinely warbled voice
Answering the stringèd noise,
   As all their souls in blissful rapture took:
The air, such pleasure loth to lose,
With thousand echoes still prolongs each heavenly close.

Nature that heard such sound
Beneath the hollow round
   Of Cynthia's seat, the airy region thrilling,
Now was almost won
To think her part was done,
   And that her reign had here its last fulfilling;
She knew such harmony alone
Could hold all Heaven and Earth in happier union.

At last surrounds their sight
A globe of circular light,
   That with long beams the shamefaced night array'd;
The helmèd cherubim
And sworded seraphim
   Are seen in glittering ranks with wings display'd,
Harping in loud and solemn quire,
With unexpressive notes to Heaven's new-born Heir.

Such music (as 'tis said)
Before was never made,
   But when of old the sons of morning sung,
While the Creator great
His constellations set,
   And the well-balanced world on hinges hung,
And cast the dark foundations deep,
And bid the weltering waves their oozy channel keep.

Ring out, ye crystal spheres,
Once bless our human ears
   (If ye have power to touch our senses so),
And let your silver chime
Move in melodious time,
   And let the bass of Heaven's deep organ blow;
And with your ninefold harmony
Make up full consort to the angelic symphony.

For if such holy song
Enwrap our fancy long,
    Time will run back and fetch the age of gold,
And speckled vanity
Will sicken soon, and die,
    And leprous sin will melt from earthly mould,
And Hell itself will pass away
And leave her dolorous mansions to the peering day.

Yea, Truth and Justice then
Will down return to men,
    Orb'd in a rainbow; and, like glories wearing,
Mercy will sit between,
Throned in celestial sheen,
    With radiant feet the tissued clouds down-steering,
And Heaven, as at some festival,
Will open wide the gates of her high palace-hall.

But wisest Fate says No,
This must not yet be so,
    The Babe lies yet in smiling infancy,
That on the bitter cross
Must redeem our loss,
    So both Himself and us to glorify:
Yet first to those ychain'd in sleep
The wakeful trump of doom must thunder through the deep,

With such a horrid clang
As on Mount Sinai rang,
    While the red fire and smouldering clouds outbrake:
The agèd Earth aghast
With terror of that blast
    Shall from the surface to the centre shake;
When at the world's last session
The dreadful Judge in middle air shall spread His throne.

[511]

And then at last our bliss
Full and perfect is,
    But now begins; for from this happy day
The old Dragon underground,
In straiter limits bound,
    Not half so far casts his usurpèd sway,
And, wroth to see his kingdom fail,
Swinges the scaly horror of his folded tail.

The oracles are dumb,
No voice or hideous hum
    Runs through the archèd roof in words deceiving.
Apollo from his shrine
Can no more divine,
    With hollow shriek the steep of Delphos leaving.
No nightly trance or breathèd spell
Inspires the pale-eyed priest from the prophetic cell.

The lonely mountains o'er,
And the resounding shore,
    A voice of weeping heard, and loud lament;
From haunted spring and dale,
Edged with poplar pale,
    The parting Genius is with sighing sent;
With flower-inwoven tresses torn
The nymphs in twilight shade of tangled thickets mourn.

In consecrated earth,
And on the holy hearth,
    The Lars and Lemures moan with midnight plaint;
In urns and altars round
A drear and dying sound
    Affrights the Flamens at their service quaint;
And the chill marble seems to sweat,
While each peculiar power forgoes his wonted seat.

Peor and Baalim
Forsake their temples dim,
   With that twice-batter'd god of Palestine;
And moonèd Ashtaroth,
Heaven's queen and mother both,
   Now sits not girt with tapers' holy shine;
The Libyc Hammon shrinks his horn,
In vain the Tyrian maids their wounded Thammuz mourn.

And sullen Moloch fled
Hath left in shadows dread
   His burning idol all of blackest hue;
In vain with cymbals' ring
They call the grisly king,
   In dismal dance about the furnace blue;
The brutish gods of Nile as fast,
Isis and Orus, and the dog Anubis, haste.

Nor is Osiris seen
In Memphian grove or green,
   Trampling the unshower'd grass with lowings loud:
Nor can he be at rest
Within his sacred chest,
   Nought but profoundest Hell can be his shroud:
In vain with timbrel'd anthems dark
The sable-stolèd sorcerers bear his worship'd ark.

He feels from Juda's land
The dreaded Infant's hand,
   The rays of Bethlehem blind his dusky eyn;
Nor all the gods beside
Longer dare abide,
   Not Typhon huge ending in snaky twine:
Our Babe, to show His Godhead true,
Can in His swaddling bands control the damnèd crew.

So when the sun in bed,
Curtain'd with cloudy red,
   Pillows his chin upon an orient wave,
The flocking shadows pale
Troop to the infernal jail,
   Each fetter'd ghost slips to his several grave,
And the yellow-skirted fays
Fly after the night-steeds, leaving their moon-loved maze.

But see! the Virgin blest
Hath laid her Babe to rest:
   Time is our tedious song should here have ending.
Heaven's youngest teemèd star
Hath fix'd her polish'd car,
   Her sleeping Lord with handmaid lamp attending:
And all about the courtly stable
Bright-harness'd angels sit in order serviceable.

JOHN MILTON (1608–74)

Verses from the Shepherds' Hymn

WE saw Thee in Thy balmy nest,
   Young dawn of our eternal day;
We saw Thine eyes break from the East,
   And chase the trembling shades away:
We saw Thee, and we blest the sight,
We saw Thee by Thine own sweet light.

Poor world, said I, what wilt thou do
   To entertain this starry stranger?
Is this the best thou canst bestow—
   A cold and not too cleanly manger?
Contend, the powers of heaven and earth,
To fit a bed for this huge birth.

[514]

Proud world, said I, cease your contest,
  And let the mighty babe alone;
The phoenix builds the phoenix' nest,
  Love's architecture is His own.
The babe, whose birth embraves this morn,
Made His own bed ere He was born.

I saw the curl'd drops, soft and slow,
  Come hovering o'er the place's head,
Off'ring their whitest sheets of snow,
  To furnish the fair infant's bed.
Forbear, said I, be not too bold;
Your fleece is white, but 'tis too cold.

I saw th' obsequious seraphim
  Their rosy fleece of fire bestow,
For well they now can spare their wings,
  Since Heaven itself lies here below.
Well done, said I; but are you sure
Your down, so warm, will pass for pure?

No, no, your King 's not yet to seek
  Where to repose His royal head;
See, see how soon His new-bloom'd cheek
  'Twixt mother's breasts is gone to bed!
Sweet choice, said we; no way but so,
Not to lie cold, yet sleep in snow!

She sings Thy tears asleep, and dips
  Her kisses in Thy weeping eye;
She spreads the red leaves of Thy lips,
  That in their buds yet blushing lie.
She 'gainst those mother diamonds tries
The points of her young eagle's eyes.

[515]

Welcome—tho' not to those gay flies,
　Gilded i' th' beams of earthly kings,
Slippery souls in smiling eyes—
　But to poor shepherds, homespun things,
Whose wealth 's their flocks, whose wit 's to be
Well read in their simplicity.

Yet, when young April's husband show'rs
　Shall bless the fruitful Maia's bed,
We'll bring the first-born of her flowers,
　To kiss Thy feet and crown Thy head.
To Thee, dread Lamb! whose love must keep
The shepherds while they feed their sheep.

To Thee, meek Majesty, soft King
　Of simple graces and sweet loves!
Each of us his lamb will bring,
　Each his pair of silver doves!
At last, in fire of Thy fair eyes,
Ourselves become our own best sacrifice!

Richard Crashaw (1613?–49)

Bermudas

Where the remote Bermudas ride
In the ocean's bosom unespied,
From a small boat that row'd along
The listening winds received this song:

　' What should we do but sing His praise
That led us through the watery maze
Unto an isle so long unknown,
　And yet far kinder than our own?
Where He the huge sea-monsters wracks,
That lift the deep upon their backs,

[516]

He lands us on a grassy stage,
Safe from the storms' and prelates' rage:
He gave us this eternal Spring
Which here enamels everything,
And sends the fowls to us in care
On daily visits through the air:
He hangs in shades the orange bright
Like golden lamps in a green night,
And does in the pomegranates 'close
Jewels more rich than Ormuz shows:
He makes the figs our mouths to meet
And throws the melons at our feet;
But apples plants of such a price,
No tree could ever bear them twice.
With cedars chosen by His hand
From Lebanon He stores the land;
And makes the hollow seas that roar
Proclaim the ambergris on shore.
He cast (of which we rather boast)
The Gospel's pearl upon our coast;
And in these rocks for us did frame
A temple where to sound His name.
Oh, let our voice His praise exalt
Till it arrive at Heaven's vault,
Which thence (perhaps) rebounding may
Echo beyond the Mexique bay!'

Thus sung they in the English boat
A holy and a cheerful note:
And all the way, to guide their chime,
With falling oars they kept the time.

ANDREW MARVELL (1621–78)

The Spacious Firmament

THE spacious firmament on high,
With all the blue ethereal sky,
And spangled heavens, a shining frame,
Their great Original proclaim.
Th' unwearied Sun from day to day
Does his Creator's power display;
And publishes to every land
The work of an Almighty hand.

Soon as the evening shades prevail,
The Moon takes up the wondrous tale;
And nightly to the listening Earth
Repeats the story of her birth:
Whilst all the stars that round her burn,
And all the planets in their turn,
Confirm the tidings as they roll,
And spread the truth from pole to pole.

What though in solemn silence all
Move round the dark terrestrial ball;
What though nor real voice nor sound
Amidst their radiant orbs be found?
In Reason's ear they all rejoice,
And utter forth a glorious voice;
For ever singing as they shine,
'The Hand that made us is divine.'

JOSEPH ADDISON (1672–1719)

Verses from 'The Song to David'

He sang of God—the mighty source
Of all things—the stupendous force
　　On which all strength depends;
From whose right arm, beneath whose eyes,
All period, power, and enterprise
　　Commences, reigns, and ends.

Tell them, I am, Jehovah said
To Moses; while earth heard in dread,
　　And, smitten to the heart,
At once above, beneath, around,
All Nature, without voice or sound,
　　Replied, O Lord, Thou art.

The world, the clustering spheres, He made;
The glorious light, the soothing shade,
　　Dale, champaign, grove, and hill;
The multitudinous abyss,
Where Secrecy remains in bliss,
　　And Wisdom hides her skill.

The pillars of the Lord are seven,
Which stand from earth to topmost heaven:
　　His Wisdom drew the plan;
His Word accomplish'd the design,
From brightest gem to deepest mine;
　　From Christ enthroned, to Man.

Sweet is the dew that falls betimes,
And drops upon the leafy limes;
　　Sweet, Hermon's fragrant air:
Sweet is the lily's silver bell,
And sweet the wakeful tapers' smell
　　That watch for early prayer.

[519]

Sweet the young nurse, with love intense,
Which smiles o'er sleeping innocence;
    Sweet, when the lost arrive:
Sweet the musician's ardour beats,
While his vague mind 's in quest of sweets,
    The choicest flowers to hive.

Strong is the horse upon his speed;
Strong in pursuit the rapid glede,
    Which makes at once his game:
Strong the tall ostrich on the ground;
Strong through the turbulent profound
    Shoots Xiphias to his aim.

Strong is the lion—like a coal
His eyeball—like a bastion's mole
    His chest against the foes:
Strong the gier-eagle on his sail;
Strong against tide th' enormous whale
    Emerges as he goes.

But stronger still, in earth and air,
And in the sea, the man of prayer,
    And far beneath the tide:
And in the seat to faith assign'd,
Where ask is have, where seek is find,
    Where knock is open wide.

Precious the penitential tear;
And precious is the sigh sincere,
    Acceptable to God:
And precious are the winning flowers,
In gladsome Israel's feast of bowers
    Bound on the hallow'd sod.

      glede] kite.   Xiphias] sword-fish.

Glorious the sun in mid career;
Glorious th' assembled fires appear;
 Glorious the comet's train:
Glorious the trumpet and alarm;
Glorious the Almighty's stretch'd-out arm;
 Glorious th' enraptured main:

Glorious the northern lights astream;
Glorious the song, when God 's the theme;
 Glorious the thunder's roar:
Glorious Hosanna from the den;
Glorious the catholic Amen;
 Glorious the martyr's gore:

Glorious—more glorious—is the crown
Of Him that brought salvation down,
 By meekness call'd thy Son:
Thou that stupendous truth believed;—
And now the matchless deed 's achieved,
 Determined, dared, and done!

CHRISTOPHER SMART (1722–71)

The Song of Honour

I CLIMBED a hill as light fell short,
And rooks came home in scramble sort,
And filled the trees and flapped and fought
And sang themselves to sleep;
An owl from nowhere with no sound
Swung by and soon was nowhere found,
I heard him calling half-way round,
Holloing loud and deep;
A pair of stars, faint pins of light,
Then many a star, sailed into sight,
And all the stars, the flower of night,

[521]

Were round me at a leap;
To tell how still the valleys lay
I heard a watchdog miles away,
And bells of distant sheep.

I heard no more of bird or bell,
The mastiff in a slumber fell,
I stared into the sky,
As wondering men have always done
Since beauty and the stars were one,
Though none so hard as I.

It seemed, so still the valleys were,
As if the whole world knelt at prayer,
Save me and me alone;
So pure and wide that silence was
I feared to bend a blade of grass,
And there I stood like stone.

There, sharp and sudden, there I heard—
   Ah ! some wild lovesick singing bird
   Woke singing in the trees ?
   The nightingale and babble-wren
   Were in the English greenwood then,
   And you heard one of these ?

The babble-wren and nightingale
Sang in the Abyssinian vale
That season of the year !
Yet, true enough, I heard them plain,
I heard them both again, again,
As sharp and sweet and clear
As if the Abyssinian tree
Had thrust a bough across the sea,
Had thrust a bough across to me
With music for my ear !

I heard them both, and oh! I heard
The song of every singing bird
That sings beneath the sky,
And with the song of lark and wren
The song of mountains, moths and men
And seas and rainbows vie!

I heard the universal choir,
The Sons of Light exalt their Sire
With universal song,
Earth's lowliest and loudest notes,
Her million times ten million throats
Exalt Him loud and long,
And lips and lungs and tongues of Grace
From every part and every place
Within the shining of His face,
The universal throng.

I heard the hymn of being sound
From every well of honour found
In human sense and soul:
The song of poets when they write
The testament of Beautysprite
Upon a flying scroll,
The song of painters when they take
A burning brush for Beauty's sake
And limn her features whole—

The song of men divinely wise
Who look and see in starry skies
Not stars so much as robins' eyes,
And when these pale away
Hear flocks of shiny pleiades
Among the plums and apple trees
Sing in the summer day—

[523]

The song of all both high and low
To some blest vision true,
The song of beggars when they throw
The crust of pity all men owe
To hungry sparrows in the snow,
Old beggars hungry too—
The song of kings of kingdoms when
They rise above their fortune Men,
And crown themselves anew—

The song of courage, heart and will
And gladness in a fight,
Of men who face a hopeless hill
With sparking and delight,
The bells and bells of song that ring
Round banners of a cause or king
From armies bleeding white—

The song of sailors every one
When monstrous tide and tempest run
At ships like bulls at red,
When stately ships are twirled and spun
Like whipping tops and help there's none
And mighty ships ten thousand ton
Go down like lumps of lead—

And song of fighters stern as they
At odds with fortune night and day,
Crammed up in cities grim and grey
As thick as bees in hives,
Hosannas of a lowly throng
Who sing unconscious of their song,
Whose lips are in their lives—

And song of some at holy war
With spells and ghouls more dread by far
Than deadly seas and cities are
Or hordes of quarrelling kings—
The song of fighters great and small,
The song of pretty fighters all
And high heroic things—

The song of lovers—who knows how
Twitched up from place and time
Upon a sigh, a blush, a vow,
A curve or hue of cheek or brow,
Borne up and off from here and now
Into the void sublime!

And crying loves and passions still
In every key from soft to shrill
And numbers never done,
Dog-loyalties to faith and friend,
And loves like Ruth's of old no end,
And intermission none—

And burst on burst for beauty and
For numbers not behind,
From men whose love of motherland
Is like a dog's for one dear hand,
Sole, selfless, boundless, blind—
And song of some with hearts beside
For men and sorrows far and wide,
Who watch the world with pity and pride
And warm to all mankind—

And endless joyous music rise
From children at their play,
And endless soaring lullabies

From happy, happy mothers' eyes,
And answering crows and baby-cries,
How many who shall say!
And many a song as wondrous well
With pangs and sweets intolerable
From lonely hearths too grey to tell,
God knows how utter grey!
And song from many a house of care
When pain has forced a footing there
And there's a Darkness on the stair
Will not be turned away—

And song—that song whose singers come
With old kind tales of pity from
The Great Compassion's lips,
That make the bells of Heaven to peal
Round pillows frosty with the feel
Of Death's cold finger tips—

The song of men all sorts and kinds,
As many tempers, moods and minds
As leaves are on a tree,
As many faiths and castes and creeds,
As many human bloods and breeds
As in the world may be;

The song of each and all who gaze
On Beauty in her naked blaze,
Or see her dimly in a haze,
Or get her light in fitful rays
And tiniest needles even,
The song of all not wholly dark,
Not wholly sunk in stupor stark
Too deep for groping Heaven—

And alleluias sweet and clear
And wild with beauty men mishear,
From choirs of song as near and dear
To Paradise as they,
The everlasting pipe and flute
Of wind and sea and bird and brute,
And lips deaf men imagine mute
In wood and stone and clay:

The music of a lion strong
That shakes a hill a whole night long,
A hill as loud as he,
The twitter of a mouse among
Melodious greenery,
The ruby's and the rainbow's song,
The nightingale's—all three,
The song of life that wells and flows
From every leopard, lark and rose
And everything that gleams or goes
Lack-lustre in the sea.

I heard it all, each, every note
Of every lung and tongue and throat,
Ay, every rhythm and rhyme
Of everything that lives and loves
And upward, ever upward moves
From lowly to sublime!
Earth's multitudinous Sons of Light,
I heard them lift their lyric might
With each and every chanting sprite
That lit the sky that wondrous night
As far as eye could climb!

I heard it all, I heard the whole
Harmonious hymn of being roll
Up through the chapel of my soul
And at the altar die,
And in the awful quiet then
Myself I heard, Amen, Amen,
Amen I heard me cry!
I heard it all and then although
I caught my flying senses, Oh,
A dizzy man was I!
I stood and stared; the sky was lit,
The sky was stars all over it,
I stood, I knew not why,
Without a wish, without a will,
I stood upon that silent hill
And stared into the sky until
My eyes were blind with stars and still
I stared into the sky.

RALPH HODGSON (b. 1872)

Prospice

FEAR death?—to feel the fog in my throat,
    The mist in my face,
When the snows begin, and the blasts denote
    I am nearing the place,
The power of the night, the press of the storm,
    The post of the foe;
Where he stands, the Arch Fear in a visible form,
    Yet the strong man must go:
For the journey is done and the summit attained,
    And the barriers fall,
Though a battle's to fight ere the guerdon be gained,
    The reward of it all.

I was ever a fighter, so—one fight more,
    The best and the last!
I would hate that death bandaged my eyes, and forbore,
    And bade me creep past.
No! let me taste the whole of it, fare like my peers
    The heroes of old,
Bear the brunt, in a minute pay glad life's arrears
    Of pain, darkness and cold.
For sudden the worst turns the best to the brave,
    The black minute 's at end,
And the elements' rage, the fiend-voices that rave,
    Shall dwindle, shall blend,
Shall change, shall become first a peace out of pain,
    Then a light, then thy breast,
O thou soul of my soul! I shall clasp thee again,
    And with God be the rest!

                 ROBERT BROWNING (1812–89)

Uphill

Does the road wind uphill all the way?
    Yes, to the very end.
Will the day's journey take the whole long day?
    From morn to night, my friend.

But is there for the night a resting-place?
    A roof for when the slow, dark hours begin.
May not the darkness hide it from my face?
    You cannot miss that inn.

Shall I meet other wayfarers at night?
    Those who have gone before.
Then must I knock, or call when just in sight?
    They will not keep you waiting at that door.

Shall I find comfort, travel-sore and weak?
    Of labour you shall find the sum.
Will there be beds for me and all who seek?
    Yea, beds for all who come.

           CHRISTINA G. ROSSETTI (1830–94)

Crossing the Bar

SUNSET and evening star,
    And one clear call for me!
And may there be no moaning of the bar,
    When I put out to sea.
But such a tide as moving seems asleep,
    Too full for sound and foam,
When that which drew from out the boundless deep
    Turns again home.

Twilight and evening bell,
    And after that the dark!
And may there be no sadness of farewell,
    When I embark;
For tho' from out our bourne of Time and Place
    The flood may bear me far,
I hope to see my Pilot face to face
    When I have crost the bar.

           ALFRED, LORD TENNYSON (1809–92)

Christ in the Universe

    WITH this ambiguous earth
His dealings have been told us. These abide:
The signal to a maid, the human birth,
The lesson, and the young Man crucified.

[530]

But not a star of all
The innumerable host of stars has heard
How He administered this terrestrial ball.
Our race have kept their Lord's entrusted Word.

Of His earth-visiting feet
None knows the secret, cherished, perilous,
The terrible, shamefast, frightened, whispered, sweet,
Heart-shattering secret of His way with us.

No planet knows that this
Our wayside planet, carrying land and wave,
Love and life multiplied, and pain and bliss,
Bears, as chief treasure, one forsaken grave.

Nor, in our little day,
May His devices with the heavens be guessed,
His pilgrimage to thread the Milky Way
Or His bestowals there be manifest.

But in the eternities,
Doubtless we shall compare together, hear
A million alien Gospels, in what guise
He trod the Pleiades, the Lyre, the Bear.

O, be prepared, my soul!
To read the inconceivable, to scan
The million forms of God those stars unroll
When, in our turn, we show to them a Man.

ALICE MEYNELL (1850–1922)

The New Ghost

' And he casting away his garment rose and came to Jesus.'

AND he cast it down, down, on the green grass,
Over the young crocuses, where the dew was—
He cast the garment of his flesh that was full of death,
And like a sword his spirit showed out of the cold sheath.

He went a pace or two, he went to meet his Lord,
And, as I said, his spirit looked like a clean sword,
And seeing him the naked trees began shivering,
And all the birds cried out aloud as it were late spring.

And the Lord came on, He came down, and saw
That a soul was waiting there for Him, one without flaw,
And they embraced in the churchyard where the robins
　　play,
And the daffodils hang down their heads, as they burn
　　away.

The Lord held his head fast, and you could see
That He kissed the unsheathed ghost that was gone free—
As a hot sun, on a March day, kisses the cold ground;
And the spirit answered, for he knew well that his peace
　　was found.

The spirit trembled, and sprang up at the Lord's word—
As on a wild, April day, springs a small bird—
So the ghost's feet lifting him up, he kissed the Lord's
　　cheek,
And for the greatness of their love neither of them could
　　speak.

But the Lord went then, to show him the way,
Over the young crocuses, under the green may
That was not quite in flower yet—to a far-distant land;
And the ghost followed, like a naked cloud holding the
   sun's hand.

FREDEGOND SHOVE

Exspecto Resurrectionem

OH! King who hast the key
      Of that dark room,
The last which prisons us but held not Thee,
      Thou know'st its gloom.
Dost Thou a little love this one
      Shut in to-night,
Young and so piteously alone,
      Cold—out of sight?
Thou know'st how hard and bare
The pillow of that new-made narrow bed,
      Then leave not there
      So dear a head!

CHARLOTTE MEW

The Quietist

I DREAMED as dream the seraphim
      Where God's white roses grew.
Then, lest I caitiff were to Him,
      I ran to draw and hew
With them that labour. So my guilt
      Seemed over; but askew
I clove the wood, and ever spilt
      The water that I drew,
      And bitter was my rue.

[533]

Then came the Master of Delight
    And softly called for me:
' Be still, be still, mine acolyte!
    My dreams are laid on thee.
It is enough, it is enough
    To hearken and to see
The secret sweetest things of Love,
    And waft felicity,—
        Yea! like a white rose-tree.'

                    RACHEL ANNAND TAYLOR

' In no Strange Land '

' The Kingdom of God is within you.'

O WORLD invisible, we view thee,
    O world intangible, we touch thee,
O world unknowable, we know thee,
    Inapprehensible, we clutch thee!

Does the fish soar to find the ocean,
    The eagle plunge to find the air—
That we ask of the stars in motion
    If they have rumour of thee there?

Not where the wheeling systems darken,
    And our benumbed conceiving soars!—
The drift of pinions, would we hearken,
    Beats at our own clay-shuttered doors.

The angels keep their ancient places;—
    Turn but a stone, and start a wing!
'Tis ye, 'tis your estrangèd faces,
    That miss the many-splendoured thing.

But (when so sad thou canst not sadder)
   Cry;—and upon thy so sore loss
Shall shine the traffic of Jacob's ladder
   Pitched betwixt Heaven and Charing Cross.

Yea, in the night, my Soul, my daughter,
   Cry,—clinging Heaven by the hems;
And lo, Christ walking on the water,
   Not of Gennesareth, but Thames!

                 FRANCIS THOMPSON (1859–1907)

Dominus Illuminatio Mea

IN the hour of death, after this life's whim,
When the heart beats low, and the eyes grow dim,
And pain has exhausted every limb—
   The lover of the Lord shall trust in Him.

When the will has forgotten the lifelong aim,
And the mind can only disgrace its fame,
And a man is uncertain of his own name—
   The power of the Lord shall fill this frame.

When the last sigh is heaved, and the last tear shed,
And the coffin is waiting beside the bed,
And the widow and child forsake the dead—
   The angel of the Lord shall lift this head.

For even the purest delight may fall,
And power must fail, and the pride must fall,
And the love of the dearest friends grow small—
   But the glory of the Lord is all in all.

        RICHARD DODDRIDGE BLACKMORE (1825–1900)

GENERAL INDEX OF FIRST LINES

[539]

PRINTED IN GREAT BRITAIN
AT THE UNIVERSITY PRESS, OXFORD
BY VIVIAN RIDLER
PRINTER TO THE UNIVERSITY